Nonexistent Compounds

Nonexistent Compounds

COMPOUNDS OF LOW STABILITY

W. E. DASENT

SENIOR LECTURER
DEPARTMENT OF CHEMISTRY
VICTORIA UNIVERSITY OF WELLINGTON, NEW ZEALAND

1965

MARCEL DEKKER, INC.

NEW YORK

First Printing: December 1965
Second Printing: August 1966

Library of Congress Catalog Number 65-27436

PRINTED IN THE UNITED STATES OF AMERICA

Preface

This book is about compounds whose structures do not offend the simpler rules of valence, but which nevertheless are characterized by a low degree of stability.

The title *Nonexistent Compounds* was chosen partly because it is a conveniently brief (if not wholly accurate) description of the contents, and partly because many of the compounds discussed have in fact never been prepared. It does not imply however that their eventual preparation is beyond all possibility, and some of them may indeed have come into being by the time this book is published.

There is of course an element of arbitrariness in deciding what constitute the "simpler rules of valence." Compounds selected for discussion range from NCl_5, whose nonexistence is fairly well understood, to $AsCl_5$, CrF_6, $SiH_2=SiH_2$, and many others where the principles responsible for their low stability are anything but straightforward. It is felt that little would be gained by attempting any definition of subject matter more restrictive than that given in the first sentence; what is intended should emerge with reasonable clarity from the ensuing chapters.

The book is an elaboration of an article with the same title published in the *Journal of Chemical Education* (**40**, 130, 1963) and as such was directed mainly at chemistry students of about senior undergraduate level, it being my conviction that from an educational viewpoint what does not happen can often be as illuminating as what does; in this expansion a more thorough account of the relevant literature is given, and the theoretical enquiry is pursued wherever possible to a somewhat greater depth. It is hoped that in this form the book may be of interest to graduate students, teachers, and research workers.

W. E. Dasent

Victoria University of Wellington,
Wellington, New Zealand

Table of Contents

Chapter 1

General Considerations

I. THERMODYNAMIC AND KINETIC ASPECTS OF STABILITY

At the outset it is profitable to pose the question "why has substance *X* never been prepared?" and to examine the principles involved in searching for its answer. The relevant principles are to be found in the separate fields of chemical *thermodynamics* and *kinetics* and are best introduced by considering some specific examples.

Suppose it is desired to prepare metallic silver by the reaction of silver chloride with hydrogen gas according to the equation

$$2\,AgCl + H_2 \rightarrow 2\,Ag + 2\,HCl \tag{1}$$

The thermodynamic or energetic requirement for the reaction to commence and continue of its own accord is that, for any infinitesimal step in the reaction, the free energies of the products (silver and hydrogen chloride) be less than the free energies of the reactants (silver chloride and hydrogen), provided the temperature and pressure are held constant. If this requirement is not satisfied then the reaction cannot proceed spontaneously beyond the stage at which the free energy change ceases to be negative. Although this restriction is quite clear-cut, a number of factors must always be considered before any decision is made concerning the energetic feasibility of a reaction.

For example, free energy data[†] for chemical substances are usually

---

[†] Thermodynamic data quoted without reference throughout this book have in general been taken from "Selected Values of Chemical Thermodynamic Properties," *Nat. Bur. of Std.* (*U.S.*), *Circ. 500*, Government Printing Office, Washington, D.C., 1952.

available as values of ΔG_f^0, the standard free energy of formation; this
quantity is the change in free energy which would occur if 1 mole of
the substance in its standard state is formed from its elements in their
standard states at 25°C. From such data the free energy change accompanying reaction (1) can be calculated as follows:

ΔG_f^0 values: Ag(s) = 0; H$_2$(g) = 0; AgCl(s) = −26.22 kcal./mole;

$$HCl(g) = -22.77 \text{ kcal./mole.}$$

$$2 \text{ AgCl(s)} + H_2(g) \rightarrow 2 \text{ Ag(s)} + 2 \text{ HCl(g)}$$

$$(2 \times -26.22) \qquad 0 \qquad\quad 0 \qquad (2 \times -22.77)$$

whence $\Delta G^0_{\text{reaction}} = (2 \times -22.77) - (2 \times -26.22) = +6.90$ kcal.

This result means that if reaction (1) were to proceed to completion
from left to right, giving 2 moles of silver metal and 2 moles of hydrogen
chloride gas at 25°C. and with the pressure maintained at 1 atmosphere,
then the free energy change would have the value $+6.90$ kcal.; the positive sign indicates that this reaction would *not* proceed to completion. It
does *not* mean that no reaction whatever would occur. The extent of any
reaction can only be gauged from the value of the equilibrium constant

$$K = \frac{p^2_{HCl}}{p_{H_2}}$$

which can be calculated from $\Delta G^0_{\text{reaction}}$ by use of the relationship

$$\Delta G^0 = -RT \ln K$$

which with $\Delta G^0 = 6900$ cal., $R = 1.987$ cal. deg.$^{-1}$ mole^{-1}, $T = 298.2°$K.,
gives $K = 8.8 \times 10^{-6}$.

It follows that if silver chloride is treated with hydrogen gas at 25°C.
and at a pressure of 1 atmosphere, reaction may ensue until the equilibrium
mixture has the composition determined by the constant evaluated above;
it is clear however that the extent of the reaction would be very small
indeed and that *under these conditions* the reaction is of no practical value.

It is still conceivable that the reaction may proceed to a significant extent
under conditions other than those to which the symbol ΔG^0 refers. For
example, ΔG^0 is a temperature-dependent quantity, and the variations
in the free energy of formation of silver chloride and hydrogen chloride
with temperature are shown in Figure 1.1.

It can be seen that in this particular case the standard free energy of formation of silver chloride increases with temperature, while that of

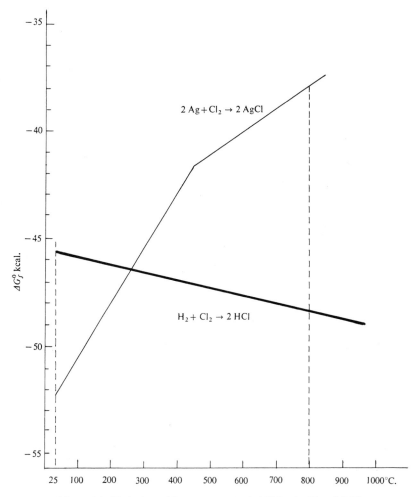

Figure 1.1. Variation with temperature of ΔG_f^0 for AgCl and HCl.

hydrogen chloride decreases, the two curves crossing at about 250°C., at which temperature the free energies of formation of the two compounds are equal. Therefore, at comparatively high temperatures, say 800°C., ΔG^0 for reaction (1) has the value $-48.4-(-37.7) = -10.7$ kcal., whence, from $\Delta G^0 = -RT \ln K$, with $\Delta G^0 = -10700$ cal. and $T = 1098°K.$,

$$K = \frac{p_{HCl}^2}{p_{H_2}} = 1.34 \times 10^2$$

corresponding to substantial conversion of silver chloride to silver metal. Thus, an increase of about 800° in the reaction temperature is sufficient in this case to cause an almost complete reversal of the energy-balance of the reaction.

Another example of the effect of altering the conditions can be seen by considering the effect of carrying out the reaction in the presence of liquid water, so that the product is aqueous hydrochloric acid:

$$2 \, AgCl(s) + H_2(g) \rightarrow 2 \, Ag(s) + 2 \, H^+(aq.) + 2 \, Cl^-(aq.) \qquad (2)$$

Since ΔG^0 for the reaction

$$2 \, HCl(g) \rightarrow 2 \, H^+(aq.) + 2 \, Cl^-(aq.)$$

is -17.2 kcal., ΔG^0 for reaction (2) is obtained by adding this quantity to ΔG^0 for reaction (1), i.e., $\Delta G_{(2)}^0 = +6.9 - 17.2 = -10.3$ kcal.

The negative value of -10.3 kcal. is in sharp contrast to the positive value $+6.9$ kcal. for the case where hydrogen chloride gas is the product, and corresponds to an equilibrium constant for reaction (2) of 3.2×10^7, i.e., virtually to complete conversion of AgCl to Ag.

It is also noteworthy that reaction (2) can be carried out using the electrochemical cell

$$\text{Pt, } H_2; \text{ HCl(aq.); AgCl; Ag}$$

for which the standard potentials for the electrodes are

$$H_2 \rightarrow 2 \, H^+ + 2e \qquad E^0 = 0.000 \text{ volt}$$
$$Ag + Cl^- \rightarrow AgCl + e \qquad E^0 = -0.222 \text{ volt}$$

so that the potential for the complete cell reaction (2) is

$$E^0 = 0.000 + 0.222 = +0.222 \text{ volt}$$

This of course corresponds to the free energy change already calculated from ΔG_f^0 values; the two quantities are related by the equation

$$\Delta G^0 = -n \, FE^0$$

which with $n = 2$, $F = 23.063$, and $E^0 = +0.222$ gives $\Delta G^0 = -10.2$ kcal.

Although the positive sign of the cell voltage $(+0.222$ volt$)$ and the corresponding negative sign of $\Delta G^0(-10.2$ kcal.$)$ indicate that reaction (2) may proceed spontaneously, they also signify that the *reverse* reaction,

$$2 \text{ Ag(s)} + 2 \text{ H}^+\text{(aq.)} + 2 \text{ Cl}^-\text{(aq.)} \rightarrow 2 \text{ AgCl(s)} + \text{H}_2\text{(g)} \qquad (3)$$

will not proceed *spontaneously* to any significant extent. Nevertheless, because of the reversible nature of the cell reaction, reaction (3) may be *made* to proceed by applying an external e.m.f. of appropriate magnitude and direction.

Thermodynamic considerations of the above sort provide information about the energetic *feasibility* of a reaction, and it must be remembered that the question of reaction *rate* is quite a separate problem. No matter how favorable thermodynamic circumstances may be, a reaction is of little use for preparative purposes unless it proceeds, or can be made to proceed, at a reasonable velocity. For example, ΔG^0_f for nitric oxide, NO, is $+20.72$ kcal./mole, i.e., for the reaction

$$\tfrac{1}{2} \text{ N}_2\text{(g)} + \tfrac{1}{2} \text{ O}_2\text{(g)} \rightarrow \text{NO(g)}$$

the standard free energy change $\Delta G^0 = +20.72$ kcal. Thus, nitric oxide is thermodynamically unstable with respect to its elements, and the value of the equilibrium constant

$$K = \frac{p_{\text{NO}}}{p_{\text{N}_2}^{\frac{1}{2}} \cdot p_{\text{O}_2}^{\frac{1}{2}}}$$

can be obtained from the expression $\Delta G^0 = -RT \ln K$ in the usual way, and has the value 6.6×10^{-16}. Obviously, the equilibrium mixture contains only a minute proportion of nitric oxide, yet it is well-known that this gas, prepared for example from acidified iron (II) sulfate and sodium nitrite solutions, shows no sign of decomposition at room temperature. The reason is of course that the *rate* of decomposition is too slow to be observed.

It is convenient to summarize the foregoing discussion. If it is proposed to prepare a compound by a certain specified reaction, then a high *negative* value for the standard free energy change ΔG^0 generally signifies that thermodynamic circumstances are favorable and that the reaction *may* proceed spontaneously, and substantially to completion. Whether the reaction will be of any practical use as a preparative method will then depend on (a) its rate being sufficiently fast, and (b) the absence of any other reactions which are even more highly favored for either thermodynamic or kinetic reasons.

A high *positive* value of ΔG^0 means in general that the reaction will not proceed of its own accord to any significant degree, under the standard conditions to which ΔG^0 refers. It may be *made* to proceed (for example by supplying the requisite energy electrolytically), or it may proceed spontaneously under different conditions, for example at other temperatures, or in other solvents.

For values of ΔG^0 close to zero, only an evaluation of the equilibrium constant will reveal the extent of a possible reaction.

The problem of an unfavorable reaction *rate* can sometimes be solved by recourse to catalysts; these do not, of course, affect the *position* of the final equilibrium.

If a compound has not previously been prepared, then as we have seen its apparent nonexistence may be due to thermodynamic or kinetic factors, and it is important in considering all such compounds to decide, if possible, which of these factors is responsible. This is easier said than done, because a vital piece of thermodynamic information — the free energy of formation of the "missing" compound — is unlikely to be known. The remainder of this chapter is devoted to a discussion of the various ways in which an estimate of the probable magnitude of the free energy of formation can sometimes be obtained.

II. ESTIMATION OF A STANDARD FREE ENERGY OF FORMATION, ΔG_f^0

The standard free energy of formation of a compound is the resultant of a heat term and an entropy term, as defined by the relationship

$$\Delta G_f^0 = \Delta H_f^0 - T \cdot \Delta S_f^0$$

where ΔG_f^0 is the free energy of formation, ΔH_f^0 is the heat (enthalpy) of formation, ΔS_f^0 is the entropy of formation, and T is the absolute temperature.

Evaluation of ΔG_f^0 usually involves the separate estimation of ΔH_f^0 and ΔS_f^0.

A. Estimates Based on Ionic Models

1. Heats of Formation. Estimates of heats of formation have been most successful for solid compounds in which the bonding is substantially ionic, i.e., where a satisfactory structural model is an assemblage of oppositely charged ions. In such cases, estimates of ΔH_f^0 can usually be obtained from Hess's Law cycles of the Born-Haber type, and ΔS_f^0 can often be evaluated approximately by using procedures developed by Latimer (1).

For example, ΔH_f^0 for a solid like sodium chloride is the change in heat content at 25°C. accompanying the reaction

$$Na(s) + \tfrac{1}{2}\, Cl_2(g) \rightarrow NaCl(s)$$

This process can be regarded as the resultant of five steps, viz.,

		sign of Δh
$Na(s) \rightarrow Na(g)$	Δh_1	+
$Na(g) \rightarrow Na^+(g) + e$	Δh_2	+
$\tfrac{1}{2}Cl_2(g) \rightarrow Cl(g)$	Δh_3	+
$Cl(g) + e \rightarrow Cl^-(g)$	Δh_4	−
$Na^+(g) + Cl^-(g) \rightarrow NaCl(s)$	Δh_5	−
$Na(s) + \tfrac{1}{2}Cl_2(g) \rightarrow NaCl(s)$	$\Sigma\, \Delta h = \Delta H$	(4)

$(\Delta h_1 + \Delta h_2)$ is usually called the standard heat of formation of the gaseous ion $Na^+(g)$, and $(\Delta h_3 + \Delta h_4)$ the standard heat of formation of the gaseous ion $Cl^-(g)$. If each of the individual Δh terms is known, or can be estimated, then ΔH_f^0 can be obtained. The five contributing terms are now discussed.

Δh_1, *the Heat of Sublimation.* Experimental heats of sublimation to monatomic gases are known for many metals, and are shown in Table 1.1.

Table 1.1

Heats of Sublimation for Metals

$\Delta H°(25°C)$, kcal./mole

Li 38.44	Be 77.9													
Na 25.9	Mg 35.6											Al 77.5		
K 21.45	Ca 42.2	Sc 93[d]	Ti 113	V 123	Cr 95	Mn 67.2	Fe 99.5	Co 101.6	Ni 102.8	Cu 81.1	Zn 30[a]	Ga 65.0[f]	Ge 89[f]	As 60[f]
Rb 19.5	Sr 39.2[f]	Y 103[d]	Zr 146	Nb 185[f]	Mo 157.5	Tc —	Ru 160[d]	Rh 138[d]	Pd 91[b]	Ag 68.4	Cd 26.5[a]	In 58.2[d]	Sn 72.0	Sb 62
Cs 18.67	Ba 42.5	La —[e]	Hf 168	Ta 186.8	W 200	Re 189[d]	Os 174[d]	Ir 165[d]	Pt 135.2	Au 88[c]	Hg 14.66	Tl 43[f]	Pb 47	Bi 49.5

Values from Lewis, G. N., and M. Randall, *Thermodynamics*, 2nd Ed., revised by K. S. Pitzer and L. Brewer, McGraw-Hill, New York, 1961, p. 672.

[a] Mann, K. H., and A. W. Tickner, *J. Phys. Chem.*, **64**, 251 (1960).

[b] Dreger, L. H., and J. L. Margrave, *J. Phys. Chem.*, **64**, 1323 (1960).

[c] Hildenbrand, D. L., and W. F. Hall, *J. Phys. Chem.*, **66**, 754 (1962).

[d] *Nat. Bur. Std. (U.S.) Circ.* 500, Washington D. C., (1952).

[e] Heats of sublimation for La and the rare earths are given by D. White, P. N. Walsh, H. W. Goldstein, and D. F. Dever, *J. Phys. Chem.*, **65**, 1409 (1961).

[f] Cottrell, T. L., *The Strengths of Chemical Bonds*, Butterworths, London, 1954.

Δh_2, *the Heat of Ionization.* Values for heats of ionization can be readily deduced from experimental ionization potentials, which are commonly tabulated as changes in internal energy ΔU at the absolute zero of temperature. Since at this temperature $\Delta U = \Delta H$, an ionization potential for the process $M(g) \rightarrow M^+(g) + e$ can be converted to a value of ΔH^0 at 25°C. by the relationship

$$\Delta H^0(25°\text{C.}) = \text{ionization potential} + \int_0^{298} [C_p(M^+) + C_p(e) - C_p(M)]dT,$$

where C_p is the heat capacity at constant pressure of the gaseous species, and T is the absolute temperature.

If the heat capacity of each of the gaseous species M, M^+, and e is taken as $5R/2$ ($R =$ gas constant), then

$$\Delta H^0(25°\text{C.}) = \text{ionization potential} + 5RT/2$$

Since $5RT/2 \approx 1.5$ kcal./mole, the correction is small.

Ionization potentials are collected in Table 1.2. Note that 1 electron volt = 23.06 kcal./mole.

Table 1.2
Ionization Potentials
0°K.; electron-volts

Element		First	Second	Third	Fourth
1	H	13.595			
2	He	24.580	54.40		
3	Li	5.390	75.62	122.42	
4	Be	9.320	18.206	153.85	217.66
5	B	8.296	25.15	37.92	259.30
6	C	11.256	24.376	47.87	67.48
7	N	14.53	29.59	47.43	77.45
8	O	13.61	35.11	54.89	77.39
9	F	17.42	34.98	62.65	87.14
10	Ne	21.559	41.07	63.5	97.02
11	Na	5.138	47.29	71.65	98.88
12	Mg	7.644	15.03	80.12	109.29
13	Al	5.984	18.82	28.44	119.96
14	Si	8.149	16.34	33.46	45.13
15	P	10.484	19.72	30.156	51.35
16	S	10.357	23.4	35.0	47.29
17	Cl	13.01	23.80	39.90	53.5
18	Ar	15.755	27.62	40.90	59.79
19	K	4.339	31.81	46	60.90
20	Ca	6.111	11.87	51.21	67
21	Sc	6.54	12.80	24.75	73.9
22	Ti	6.82	13.57	27.47	43.24
23	V	6.74	14.65	29.31	48
24	Cr	6.763	16.49	30.95	49.6
25	Mn	7.432	15.64	33.69	
26	Fe	7.90	16.18	30.64	
27	Co	7.86	17.05	33.49	
28	Ni	7.633	18.15	36.16	
29	Cu	7.724	20.29	36.83	
30	Zn	9.391	17.96	39.70	
31	Ga	6.00	20.51	30.70	64.2
32	Ge	7.88	15.93	34.21	45.7
33	As	9.81	18.63	28.34	50.1
34	Se	9.75	21.5	32.0	42.9
35	Br	11.84	21.6	35.9	47.3
36	Kr	13.996	24.56	36.9	
37	Rb	4.176	27.5	40	

Table 1.2 (continued)

Element	First	Second	Third	Fourth
38 Sr	5.692	11.03		57
39 Y	6.38	12.23	20.51	
40 Zr	6.984	13.13	22.98	34.33
41 Nb	6.88	14.32	25.04	38.3
42 Mo	7.10	16.15	27.13	46.4
43 Tc	7.28	15.26		
44 Ru	7.364	16.76	28.46	
45 Rh	7.46	18.07	31.05	
46 Pd	8.33	19.42	32.92	
47 Ag	7.574	21.48	34.82	
48 Cd	8.991	16.90	37.47	
49 In	5.785	18.86	28.03	54.4
50 Sn	7.342	14.63	30.49	40.72
51 Sb	8.639	16.5	25.3	44.1
52 Te	9.01	18.6	31	38
53 I	10.454	19.09		
54 Xe	12.127	21.2	32.1	
55 Cs	3.893	25.1		
56 Ba	5.210	10.001		
57 La	5.61	11.43	19.17	
72 Hf		14.9		
73 Ta	7.88			
74 W	7.98			
75 Re	7.87			
76 Os	8.7			
77 Ir	9			
78 Pt	9.0	18.56		
79 Au	9.22	20.5		
80 Hg	10.43	18.751	34.2	
81 Tl	6.106	20.42	29.8	50.7
82 Pb	7.415	15.03	31.93	42.31
83 Bi	7.287	16.68	25.56	45.3
84 Po	8.43			
86 Rn	10.75			
88 Ra	5.277	10.144		
89 Ac		12.1		

Data from Moore, C. E., *"Atomic Energy Levels,"* *Nat. Bur. Std. Circ. 467*, Vol. 1 (1949); Vol. 2, (1952); Vol. 3, (1958), Washington, D.C.

Δh_3, *the Heat of Atomization.* Experimental values for heats of atomization of elements from standard states to monatomic gases are given in Table 1.3.

Table 1.3

Heats of Atomization of Elements from Standard States to Monatomic Gases
$$\Delta H^\circ, \text{ kcal./gram-atom (3)}$$

H	C	N	O	F
52.09	170.9	113.0	59.55	18.9
	Si		S	Cl
	108		66.4	28.94
			Se	Br
			49.4	26.76
				I
				25.52

Δh_4. Energy values for this term are commonly tabulated as *electron affinities* which, like ionization potentials, usually refer to changes in internal energy at the absolute zero of temperature. If this is the case a similar correction should be made to obtain $\Delta H^\circ(25°C.)$, viz.,

$$X(g) + e \rightarrow X^-(g)$$

$$\Delta H^\circ(25°C.) = \text{electron affinity} + \int_0^{298} \left[C_p(X^-) - C_p(X) - C_p(e) \right] dT$$

$$= \text{electron affinity} - 5RT/2, \quad T = 298°K.$$

It should be noted that in energy cycles involving both an ionization potential and an electron affinity, such as (4), the correcting terms $5RT/2$ cancel out, and no correction need therefore be made.

Direct experimental determinations of electron affinities have been made for only a few atoms, for example (2):

$H(g) + e \rightarrow H^-(g)$	$\Delta H^\circ(25°C.) = 17.8 \text{ kcal./mole}$
$F(g) + e \rightarrow F^-(g)$	83.5
$Cl(g) + e \rightarrow Cl^-(g)$	87.3
$Br(g) + e \rightarrow Br^-(g)$	82.0
$I(g) + e \rightarrow I^-(g)$	75.7

In many instances, especially in polyatomic radicals, the direct experimental determination of energy changes for processes such as $SO_4(g)+2e \rightarrow SO_4^{2-}(g)$ is rarely possible. In some cases the problem can be circumvented in the following way: Where the heat of formation of a compound is known, and its lattice energy (see Δh_5, next section) can be estimated, the standard heat of formation ΔH_f^0 of a *gaseous ion* can be derived. For example, ΔH_f^0 for sodium borohydride, $NaBH_4(s)$, is known (4) and has the value -45.5 kcal./mole; its lattice energy has been estimated by Altshuller (5) as 168 kcal./mole. Hence from the cycle

$$
\begin{array}{ll}
Na(s) \rightarrow Na(g) & \Delta h_1 \\
Na(g) \rightarrow Na^+(g)+e & \Delta h_2 \\
B(s)+2\,H_2(g)+e \rightarrow BH_4^-(g) & \Delta h_3 \\
Na^+(g)+BH_4^-(g) \rightarrow NaBH_4(s) & \Delta h_4 \\
\hline
Na(s)+B(s)+2\,H_2(g) \rightarrow NaBH_4(s) & \Delta H_f^0,\ NaBH_4(s)
\end{array}
$$

$$
\begin{aligned}
\Delta h_3 = \Delta H_f^0,\ BH_4^-(g) &= \Delta H_f^0,\ NaBH_4(s) - \Delta h_1 - \Delta h_2 - \Delta h_4 \\
&= -45.5 - 25.9 - 118.4 - (-168) \\
&= -21.8\ \text{kcal./mole}
\end{aligned}
$$

From similar calculations on a number of alkali metal borohydrides, the approximate mean value ΔH_f^0, $BH_4^-(g) = -23 \pm 5$ kcal./mole has been derived (6). This value may then be used in energy cycles for other borohydrides.

Heats of formation for a number of gaseous anions, estimated in this way, are shown in Table 1.4. Evaluation of the electron affinity itself from these data requires a knowledge of the dissociation energies of the bonds in the uncharged radical, and these are available in only a few cases (such as O_2).

Table 1.4
Standard Heats of Formation ΔH_f^0 of Gaseous Anions (6)
(kcal. /mole)

O^{2-}	217	OH^-	50	BH_4^-	-23
S^{2-}	152	SH^-	-31	BF_4^-	-406
Se^{2-}	165	CN^-	7	NO_3^-	-81
Te^{2-}	145	N_3^-	35	CNO^-	-63
HF_2^-	150				

Δh_5, *the Lattice Enthalpy*. This term cannot be measured directly. "Experimental" lattice enthalpies are those obtained indirectly from Born-Haber cycle calculations in cases where heats of formation are known.

The lattice *energy*, as usually defined, is the change in internal energy ΔU at the absolute zero of temperature which accompanies the process

$$NaCl(s) \rightarrow Na^+(g) + Cl^-(g) \tag{5}$$

It is related to the lattice enthalpy at 25°C. as follows:

$$\Delta H^0(25°C.) = \text{lattice energy} + \int_0^{298} [C_p(Na^+) + C_p(Cl^-) - C_p(NaCl)]dT$$

where C_p is the heat capacity at constant pressure and T is the absolute temperature.

In approximate calculations it is often assumed that the lattice energy does not change significantly with temperature, and that therefore

$$\Delta H^0(25°C.) = \text{lattice energy} + 2RT, \quad T = 298°K.$$

Also, the level of accuracy of some estimates is such that the correcting term $2RT$ (≈ 1.2 kcal./mole) is ignored.

Calculation of Lattice Energies. The simplest expressions for calculating a lattice energy are obtained by considering two contributing terms: (1) That arising from the Coulomb interaction between the oppositely charged ions in the crystal, for which the potential energy is

$$\frac{NMz_1 z_2 e^2}{r}$$

N is Avogadro's number; z_1, z_2 are the ion valences; e is the electronic charge; r is the distance between oppositely charged ions; and M is the Madelung constant, a number depending solely on the crystal geometry. (2) That arising from repulsive forces due to interpenetration of the charge clouds of the ions (Born repulsion). These forces increase very rapidly as r decreases; their contribution to the energy has been assumed proportional to either (a) $1/r^n$, (7), where n is a constant; (for the alkali metal halides, n has values from about 6 to 10); or preferably to (b) $\exp^{-r/\rho}$, (8) where ρ is a constant. Its value is commonly assumed to be 0.345 when the internuclear distance is expressed in Angstrom units. The expression for the lattice energy is then

$$\text{lattice energy } U = \frac{NMz_1 z_2 e^2}{r} - k \exp^{-r/\rho}$$

The constant k can be eliminated by using the fact that at the equilibrium distance of separation between the ions r_0

$$\frac{dU}{dr} = 0 \qquad (r = r_0)$$

whence

$$U = \frac{NMz_1z_2e^2}{r_0}\left(1 - \frac{\rho}{r_0}\right)$$

This simple expression is capable of considerable refinement; the more rigorous expressions are of the form

$$U = U_M - U_R + U_L - U_Z \tag{6}$$

in which U_M (the Madelung term) arises from the electrostatic attraction between the oppositely charged ions; U_R (the repulsive energy term) accounts for the repulsions arising from the interpenetration of the charge clouds of the ions; U_L (the London or dispersion energy term) allows for the dispersion forces (van der Waals attractions) between the ions, and is of the form c/r^6, with c a constant; U_Z is the zero-point energy of the crystal. In (6) the symbols stand for the numerical values of the energy quantities concerned. Extended term-by-term calculations of lattice energies are described in Waddington's (6) review. In the case of crystals containing a nonspherical ion, it is no longer justified to treat such an ion as a point charge, and an additional energy term U_Q (6) to allow for the effect of the electrical multipole should be added to (6).

Typical contributions of the various terms to the total lattice energy are shown in Table 1.5.

Table 1.5
Contributing Terms to Total Lattice Energy
(kcal./mole)

	U	$=$	U_M	$-$	U_R	$+$	U_L	$-$	U_Z	$+$	U_Q
NaCl	183		206		23.8		3.0		1.8		0
CuCl	216		232		29.8		15.2		1.2		0
AgCl	202		209		34.5		29.2		1.3		0
KHF$_2$	152		168		33.0		7.1		1.0		11.3

Before any substantial progress can be made towards the calculation of a lattice energy, it is necessary to know, or to be able to estimate, both the internuclear distance (r_0) in the crystal and the type of crystal structure adopted (and hence the Madelung constant). For compounds whose structure has not been determined neither of these factors can be known exactly. In such cases the internuclear distance r_0 can be taken approximately as the sum of the radii of the constituent ions, and the crystal structure can sometimes be guessed, making use of radius-ratio rules (9) and inferences from analogous compounds of known structure.

Techniques for making approximate lattice energy calculations in cases where crystallographic data are lacking have been developed by Kapustinskii (10). His generalized equation, applicable to all types of crystal, is

$$U = \frac{287.2\, v z_1 z_2}{r_c + r_a} \left(1 - \frac{0.345}{r_c + r_a} \right) \tag{7}$$

in which v is the number of ions in the simplest formula or "molecule" of the substance, and r_c, r_a are the crystal radii of the cation and anion, whose sum is assumed to give the internuclear distance. The status of this equation has been discussed by Waddington (6); it is of value for rough approximations in situations where the data necessary for more rigorous treatments are inaccessible. Furthermore, by making use of data for compounds whose experimental lattice energies (deduced from heats of formation) are known, it is possible to use equation (7) to evaluate the radii of many ions, including complex ions, for which values were previously unknown. Many of these "thermochemical radii" have been estimated by Yatsimirskii (11), and a compilation of them is given in Table 1.6. Radii for other ions are available from the well-known values of Goldschmidt and Pauling. In cases where the Goldschmidt and Pauling values differ, the decision as to which to use in Kapustinskii's equation is of course largely arbitrary, and is an obvious limitation on the equation's accuracy.

Extensive estimates of heats of formation, using Kapustinskii's methods for obtaining lattice energies, have been made for the halides (12) and the chalcogenides (26) of the transition elements of the first long period.

There is an additional refinement which can be made for crystals which contain a transition metal ion with an incomplete d electron subshell; in these cases the energies of the five d orbitals, which are degenerate in the free (gas-phase) ion, are altered by the field of the anion in the crystal in such a way as to produce a stabilization, called the crystal field stabilization energy. Allowance for this effect results in improved agreement between calculated and experimental lattice energies in many cases (13,14).

Table 1.6
Thermochemical Radii (Å)

OH^-	NO_2^-	NO_3^-	BO_3^{3-}			
1.40	1.55	1.89	1.91			
ClO_3^-	BrO_3^-	IO_3^-				
2.00	1.91	1.82				
CN^-	CNO^-	CNS^-				
1.82	1.59	1.95				
HCO_3^-	CO_3^{2-}					
1.63	1.85					
SO_4^{2-}	CrO_4^{2-}	MoO_4^{2-}	PO_4^{3-}	ClO_4^-	MnO_4^-	AsO_4^{3-}
2.30	2.40	2.54	2.38	2.36	2.40	2.48
BF_4^-						
2.28						

The accuracy achieved in calculating lattice energies by the various procedures described above is of course rather heavily dependent upon the pertinence to the case considered of the ionic model adopted. Extensive comparative tables of calculated and experimental lattice energies are available (6), and illustrate the degree of agreement that can be expected. The most marked departures from calculated values are shown by compounds in which covalent contributions to the binding energy are to be expected; the well-known rules of Fajans often provide a useful aid to the recognition of cases where covalency is to be expected, e.g., in crystals where the cation is small and highly charged, or the anion large and highly charged. Some empirical equations which allow for the effect of partial covalent character in bonds have been developed by Yatsimirskii (15).

2. Entropies of Formation. To evaluate the term $T\Delta S_f^0$ in the expression for the free energy of formation of a substance, a knowledge of the absolute entropy S^0 of each reactant and product is required. Approximate procedures for obtaining the entropies of ionic solids have been developed by Latimer (1); he assigned average values to the contributions made by metals and anions to the total entropy S^0 of the solid. Some of these values are shown in Table 1.7.

Table 1.7
Entropy Contribution of Metals in Solid Compounds at 25°C.
(cal./mole deg.)

Be													
4.3													

Mg	Al												
7.6	8.0												

Ca	Sc	Ti	V	Cr	Mn	Fe	Co	Ni	Cu	Zn	Ga	Ge	As
9.3	9.7	9.8	10.1	10.2	10.3	10.4	10.6	10.5	10.8	10.9	11.2	11.3	11.45
Sr	Y	Zr	Nb	Mo	Tc	Ru	Rh	Pd	Ag	Cd	In	Sn	Sb
12.0	12.0	12.1	12.2	12.3	—	12.5	12.5	12.7	12.8	12.9	13.0	13.1	13.2
Ba	La	Hf	Ta	W	Re	Os	Ir	Pt	Au	Hg	Tl	Pb	Bi
13.7	13.8	14.8	14.9	15.0	15.0	15.1	15.2	15.2	15.3	15.4	15.4	15.5	15.6

Entropy Contributions of Negative Ions in Solid Compounds at 25°C.
(cal./mole deg.)

	Charge on cation			
	+1	+2	+3	+4
F^-	5.5	4.7	4.0	5.0
Cl^-	10.0	8.1	6.9	8.1
Br^-	13.0	10.9	9	10
I^-	14.6	13.6	12.5	13.0
O^{2-}	2.4	0.5	0.5	1.0
S^{2-}	8.2	5.0	1.3	2.5
OH^-	5.0	4.5	3.0	
CN^-	7.2	6		
NO_2^-	17.8	15		
NO_3^-	21.7	17.7	15	14
CO_3^{2-}	15.2	11.4	8	
HCO_3^-	17.4	13	10	
ClO_3^-	24.9	20		
BrO_3^-	26.5	22.9	19	
IO_3^-	25.5	22.9	19	
MnO_4^-	31.8	28		
ClO_4^-	26.0	22		
SO_3^{2-}	19	14.9	11	
SO_4^{2-}	22	17.2	13.7	12
CrO_4^{2-}	26.2	21		
$C_2O_4^{2-}$	22	17.7	14	
PO_4^{3-}	24	17.0	12	

The estimated entropy S^0 of barium sulfate, $BaSO_4(s)$, at 25°C. is, for example,

Ba	13.7
SO_4	17.2
S^0	$= 30.9$ cal./mole deg.

S^0 (expt.) $= 31.6$ cal./mole deg.

For a complex salt such as K_2IrCl_6, the contribution chosen for Cl is that corresponding to the average charge on the metals (2 K^+, Ir^{4+}, average charge $= 2+$). Hence

2 K	18.4
Ir	15.2
6 Cl	48.6
S^0	$= 82.2$ cal./mole deg.

The problems associated with the estimation of the entropies of liquid and gaseous compounds have been discussed by Kubaschewski and Evans (25). In the case of *gases*, the following entirely empirical (25) equations, relating the entropy S^0 (25°C.) to the molecular weight M, enable rough estimates to be made.

Diatomic gases:

$$S^0 = 53.8 + 0.043M - 240M^{-1}$$

Polyatomic gases:

$$S^0 = 39.0 + 0.34M - (6.2 \times 10^{-4})M^2$$

3. Examples of Calculations. Two examples of the calculation of heats of formation by the methods described in the preceding sections will now be given. The lattice energy is evaluated in the first case by the crudest sort of approximation, and in the second by an extended and more rigorous calculation. In the second case the entropy term ΔS_f^0 is also assessed, enabling the estimation of a free energy of formation.

(a) *The Heat of Formation of Sodium Dibromide.* Grimm and Herzfeld (16), as long ago as 1923, estimated the heats of formation of hypothetical crystals like $CaCl$, $LiCl_2$, and KF_2 from a Born-Haber type of treatment. Their procedure is now illustrated for sodium dibromide,

$NaBr_2 = Na^{2+}$, $2\ Br^-$. All the heat quantities required are known except the lattice enthalpy. The radius of the ion Na^{2+} is not of course known, so that the inter-ionic distances in the crystal (whose structure must be assumed on some reasonable basis) are also unknown. Grimm and Herzfeld therefore equated the lattice energy of $NaBr_2$ with that of its periodic group neighbor, $MgBr_2$. Now the experimental (6) lattice energy of $MgBr_2$, deduced from its heat of formation, is 575 kcal./mole. Since the *calculated* lattice energy (6) for the same compound is 513 kcal./mole, the difference (62 kcal./mole) presumably arises from a contribution from covalent bonding forces. In equating the lattice energies of $NaBr_2$ and $MgBr_2$, the assumptions made are that the covalent forces in each crystal are the same, that $NaBr_2$ has the same (cadmium iodide) structure as $MgBr_2$, and that the radius of the ion Na^{2+} is the same as that of Mg^{2+}, i.e., that the internuclear distances in the two crystals are identical. These assumptions are, of course, of the grossest sort. Nevertheless, in spite of a large possible error in the lattice energy assumed for $NaBr_2$, useful information can be deduced from the calculated heat of formation. In calculations at this level of approximation, energies and enthalpies referring to different temperatures may be used without correction:

	ΔH
$Na(s) \rightarrow Na(g)$	$+\ \ \ 26$
$Na(g) \rightarrow Na^{2+}(g) + 2e$	$+1212$
$Br_2(l) \rightarrow 2\ Br(g)$	$+\ \ \ 53$
$2\ Br(g) + 2e \rightarrow 2\ Br^-(g)$	$-\ 164$
$Na^{2+}(g) + 2\ Br^-(g) \rightarrow NaBr_2(s)$	$-\ 575$
$Na(s) + Br_2(l) \rightarrow NaBr_2(s)$	$+\ 552$ kcal./mole

It can be seen that the heat of formation of sodium dibromide has a very large positive value, whose significance is unaffected by a considerable uncertainty in the value of the contributing lattice enthalpy term. If the entropy change ΔS is ignored, and its value in this case would be relatively small, it follows that $NaBr_2$ must be highly unstable with respect to its elements, and also with respect to disproportionation in the sense

$$NaBr_2(s) \rightarrow NaBr(s) + \tfrac{1}{2}\ Br_2(l)$$

The instability in $NaBr_2$, as compared to NaBr, is obviously due to the fact that the enormous energy required to remove a second electron from the Na^+ ion ($Na \rightarrow Na^+ + e$, 118 kcal./mole; $Na^+ \rightarrow Na^{2+} + e$, 1090 kcal./mole) is only partly offset by the increase in lattice energy ($NaBr$, 176 kcal./mole; $NaBr_2$, 575 kcal./mole).

(b) *The Free Energy of Formation of Gold* (I) *Fluoride, AuF.* Gold (I) fluoride is the only halide of unipositive gold whose existence has not been definitely established, and Waddington (17) sought thermodynamic evidence for its nonexistence by calculating its free energy of formation. ΔH_f^0 was estimated from a Born-Haber cycle, and ΔS_f^0 by Latimer's (1) procedure.

The Heat of Formation of AuF. The only term in the Born-Haber cycle for AuF whose value is not known experimentally is the lattice enthalpy, and this was obtained as follows: The assumption of an essentially ionic lattice for AuF was considered justified because of the agreement, within 10 kcal./mole, between the calculated and experimental lattice energies for the related and well-known compound silver fluoride, AgF. A sodium chloride lattice for AuF was assumed since AgF has such a structure, although in both cases the radius ratios suggest a cesium chloride structure. The internuclear distance in AuF was computed using Pauling's radii for the ions, viz., $r_{Au^+} = 1.37\,\text{Å}$, $r_{F^-} = 1.36\,\text{Å}$; $r_{Au^+} + r_{F^-} = 2.73\,\text{Å}$, and Ladd's and Lee's (18) expression for the lattice energy (successfully used for AgF) evaluated, giving 186 kcal./mole for the lattice enthalpy at 25°C. Hence:

	ΔH
$Au(s) \rightarrow Au(g)$	$+\ 88$
$Au(g) \rightarrow Au^+(g) + e$	$+214$
$\frac{1}{2} F_2(g) \rightarrow F(g)$	$+\ 19$
$F(g) + e \rightarrow F^-(g)$	$-\ 84$
$Au^+(g) + F^-(g) \rightarrow AuF(s)$	-186
$Au(s) + \frac{1}{2} F_2(g) \rightarrow AuF(s)$	$+\ 51$ kcal./mole,

i.e., ΔH_f^0 for AuF $= +51$ kcal./mole; the compound is thus endothermic.

The Entropy of Formation of AuF. The entropy of AuF can be estimated by using Latimer's (1) values of 5.5 cal./deg. for a fluoride ion in a monovalent fluoride, and 15.3 cal./deg. for the ion Au^+, i.e.,

$$S^0 \text{ for AuF} = 5.5 + 15.3$$

$$= 20.8 \text{ cal./deg. per mole}$$

Since S^0 for Au(s) = 11.4 cal./deg., and S^0 for $\frac{1}{2}$ F_2(g) = 24.3 cal./deg., ΔS_f^0 for the process

$$Au(s) + \frac{1}{2} F_2(g) \rightarrow AuF(s)$$

is $20.8 - (11.4 + 24.3) = -14.9$ cal./deg. per mole.

The *free energy of formation* of AuF at 25°C. is thus

$$\Delta G_f^0 = \Delta H_f^0 - T \cdot \Delta S_f^0$$

$$= +51 - \frac{(298 \times -14.9)}{1000} = +56 \text{ kcal./mole}$$

This large positive value establishes that gold (1) fluoride is unstable with respect to its elements at 25°C., i.e., that the reasons for its non-existence are thermodynamic in character.

A similar treatment of the monohalides of chromium has been given by Petrakis (27).

B. Ionic-Model Calculations for Covalent Compounds

Some attempts have been made to calculate binding energies (and hence heats of formation) for gas-phase molecules, using the equations of classical electrostatics applied to a fully ionic model. For example, a molecule like boron trifluoride is treated as three trigonally-arranged fluoride ions surrounding, and polarized by, a central B^{3+} ion. The potential energy of such a system (with the potential energy of the infinitely-separated ions taken as zero) is taken as ΔH^0 for the process

$$B^{3+}(g) + 3 F^-(g) \rightarrow BF_3(g) \tag{8}$$

and the parameters required for its evaluation are the internuclear distances and the polarizability of the fluoride ion. In this way Garrick (19) calculated a number of binding energies for fluorides and chlorides, using the Goldschmidt ionic radii to estimate the internuclear distances. In many cases, e.g., BF_3, AlF_3, PF_5, SF_6, $AlCl_3$, $SiCl_4$, and $SnCl_4$, the results were within about 6 % of the values deduced from experimental heats of formation. For example, Garrick's estimate of ΔH^0 for reaction (8) = 1910 kcal./mole, and this can be compared with the experimental value obtained as follows:

$$B(s) \rightarrow B(g) \qquad\qquad\qquad \Delta h_1$$
$$B(g) \rightarrow B^{3+}(g) + 3e \qquad\qquad \Delta h_2$$
$$1\tfrac{1}{2}\, F_2(g) \rightarrow 3\, F(g) \qquad\qquad \Delta h_3$$
$$3\, F(g) + 3e \rightarrow 3\, F^-(g) \qquad\qquad \Delta h_4$$
$$B^{3+}(g) + 3\, F^-(g) \rightarrow BF_3(g) \qquad \Delta h_5$$

$$\overline{B(s) + 1\tfrac{1}{2}\, F_2(g) \rightarrow BF_3(g) \qquad\qquad \Delta H_f^0}$$

$$\Delta h_5 = \Delta H_f^0 - (\Delta h_1 + \Delta h_2 + \Delta h_3 + \Delta h_4)$$

Upon inserting known experimental values,

$$\Delta h_5 = -265 - (141 + 1639 + 55 - 250)$$
$$= -1850 \ \text{kcal./mole}$$

The difference is thus $1910 - 1850 = 60$ kcal./mole, or about 3% of the experimental value. Although in some respects this discrepancy may seem small for a method based on so crude a model, it must be noted that if Δh_5 is calculated by Garrick's procedure for the purpose of estimating a heat of formation, then an error of 60 kcal./mole in Δh_5 will of course produce a similar error in ΔH_f^0. That is, if ΔH_f^0 for $BF_3(g)$ is estimated using experimental values for Δh_1, Δh_2, Δh_3, and Δh_4, and Garrick's value for Δh_5, the result

$$\Delta H_f^0 = 325 \ \text{kcal./mole}$$

differs from the experimental result by 60 kcal./mole, or about 22%, which is too big a discrepancy for the method to be of much value in this case.

The application of the ionic model to transition-metal complexes, including a discussion of crystal field corrections, has been described by Basolo and Pearson (20), and a general survey of the treatment of molecules as electrostatic systems is that of Van Arkel and De Boer (21).

C. Estimates Based on Covalent Models

As shown in Section IIa of this chapter the estimation of ΔH_f^0 for an ionic solid involves, inter alia, the assessment of a lattice enthalpy term, and procedures for doing this are available for crystals in which the bonding is assumed to be ionic. For compounds where this assumption is unjustified, the problem of estimating ΔH_f^0 can be approached through a rather different energy cycle.

Suppose it is desired to estimate the heat of formation of tetrazan, $H_2N \cdot NH \cdot NH \cdot NH_2$, assuming the compound to be gaseous in its standard state. Then ΔH_f^0 is the change in heat content for the process

$$2\,N_2(g) + 3\,H_2(g) \rightarrow N_4H_6(g)$$

which can be regarded as the resultant of the steps

$$
\begin{array}{ll}
2\,N_2(g) \rightarrow 4\,N(g) & \Delta h_1 \\
3\,H_2(g) \rightarrow 6\,H(g) & \Delta h_2 \\
4\,N\,(g) + 6\,H(g) \rightarrow N_4H_6(g) & \Delta h_3
\end{array}
$$

Of these energy steps, Δh_1 and Δh_2 can be evaluated from the experimentally determined heats of atomization of nitrogen and hydrogen. These and other data used in this section are included in Table 1.8. However, Δh_3 is not so readily evaluated; it represents the heat liberated when six N—H covalent bonds and three N—N covalent bonds are formed from the constituent atoms:

$$
4\,N + 6\,H \rightarrow \quad
\begin{array}{c}
H \qquad\qquad\quad H \\
\diagdown \qquad\qquad\quad \diagup \\
N{-}N{-}N{-}N \\
\diagup \quad | \quad | \quad \diagdown \\
H \quad\;\; H \; H \quad\;\; H
\end{array}
$$

There are no straightforward methods available for evaluating Δh_3. The usual procedure is to attempt to evaluate the "bond energy" of the various bonds formed; the significance of this term will now be discussed.

Table 1.8
Heats of Formation (25°C., kcal./mole) From Standard States

N(g)	+113.0
H(g)	+ 52.09
$NH_3(g)$	− 11.09
$N_2H_4(g)$	+ 22.1

The mean *thermochemical bond energy* (or simply *bond energy*) of the N—H bond, $\bar{D}_{N-H}$, is one-third of the heat necessary to break all three N—H bonds in ammonia

$$NH_3(g) \rightarrow N(g) + 3\,H(g), \qquad \Delta H = 3\,\bar{D}_{N-H}$$

The temperature referred to is usually 25°C. Since $\Delta H = 280.4$ kcal./mole, $\bar{D}_{N-H} = 93.4$ kcal./mole.

It must be emphasized that the thermochemical bond energy is a mean quantity, and that the energy required to break an individual N—H bond may be different from this mean. The energy required to break an individual bond is called the *bond-dissociation energy*, and is strictly the change in internal energy accompanying the bond fission reaction at absolute zero, $0°K$. For example, for the first N—H bond in ammonia, D_{H_2N-H} is the change in internal energy for the reaction

$$NH_3(g) \rightarrow NH_2(g) + H(g) \qquad \text{at } 0°K$$

This energy quantity differs only slightly from ΔH^0 at 25°C., and the accuracy of many experimental data is such as to make the distinction unwarranted. The stepwise bond-dissociation energies for the three bonds in ammonia are (22)

$$\text{kcal./mole}$$
$$NH_3(g) \rightarrow NH_2(g) + H(g) \qquad D_{H_2N-H} = 107$$
$$NH_2(g) \rightarrow NH(g) + H(g) \qquad D_{HN-H} = 88$$
$$NH(g) \rightarrow N(g) + H(g) \qquad D_{N-H} = 85$$

It can be seen that the individual bond-dissociation energies differ markedly from their mean value, 93.3 kcal./mole, i.e, the energy of a bond depends on its molecular environment.

Mean thermochemical bond energies are listed in Table 1.9.

Table 1.9
Mean Thermochemical Bond Energies
(kcal./mole, 25°C.)

(a) *X—X bonds*

		H—H		
		104.2		
B—B	C—C	N—N	O—O	F—F
79.1 [a]	83.1	38.4	33.2	36.6
	Si—Si	P—P	S—S	Cl—Cl
	42.2	51.3	50.9	58.0
	Ge—Ge	As—As	Se—Se	Br—Br
	37.6	32.1	44.0	46.1
	Sn—Sn	Sb—Sb	Te—Te	I—I
	34.2	30.2	33	36.1
		Bi—Bi		
		25		

Table 1.9 (continued)

(b) *X—H bonds*

C—H	N—H	O—H	F—H
98.8	93.4	110.6	134.6
Si—H	P—H	S—H	Cl—H
70.4	76.4	81.1	103.2
	As—H	Se—H	Br—H
	58.6	66.1	87.5
		Te—H	I—H
		57.5	71.4

(c) *X—C bonds*

	N—C	O—C	F—C
	69.7	84.0	105.4
Si—C		S—C	Cl—C
69.3		62.0	78.5
			Br—C
			65.9
			I—C
			57.4

(d) *X—hal. bonds*

Si—F	Si—Cl	Si—Br	Si—I
129.3	85.7	69.1	50.9
N—F	Ge—Cl	P—Br	As—I
64.5	97.5	65.4	41.6
As—F	N—Cl	As—Br	P—I
111.3	47.7	56.5	51.4
O—F	P—Cl	S—Br	
44.2	79.1	50.7	
Cl—F	As—Cl	I—Br	
60.6	68.9	42.5	
	O—Cl		
	48.5		
	S—Cl		
	59.7		
	Br—Cl		
	52.3		
	I—Cl		
	50.3		

Table 1.9 (continued)

(e) *Miscellaneous*

	Si—O	Si—S
	88.2	54.2

ᵃ from reference (24); other data from reference (2).

[a] from reference (24); other data from reference (2).

(It is important to realize that both mean thermochemical bond energies and bond-dissociation energies normally refer to processes in which both reactants and products are in their ground states. For example, the enthalpy change for the reaction

$$B(g)+3\ F(g) \rightarrow BF_3(g), \qquad \Delta H(25°C.) = -461 \text{ kcal./mole} \qquad (9)$$

yields a mean B—F bond energy of 154 kcal./mole. In this reaction, the B and F atoms are in their ground electronic states: s^2p^1 for the boron atom, and s^2p^5 for the fluorine atoms. It is improbable that these unmodified atomic orbitals are used for bond formation, and the energies of suitable hybrid bonding orbitals (mixtures of s and p) have been estimated by Cotton and Leto (23). One can then regard reaction (9) as proceeding in two steps,

$$B(g)+3\ F(g) \rightarrow B^*(g)+3\ F^*(g) \qquad \Delta h_1$$

and

$$B^*(g)+3\ F^*(g) \rightarrow BF_3(g) \qquad \Delta h_2$$

in which the symbols B* and F* refer to excited atoms with their orbitals "prepared" for bond formation. The excitation energy Δh_1 was estimated (23) as $+213$ kcal., and Δh_2, called the *intrinsic* bond energy, $= \Delta H - \Delta h_1 = -461 - 213 = -674$ kcal. for three B—F bonds.)

In calculating the heat of formation of tetrazan, it is necessary to assume that the six N—H bonds in N_4H_6 have the mean $\bar{D}_{N-H}$ value, viz., 93.4 kcal./mole. Also required is a value for $\bar{D}_{N-N}$, and this is derived from the heat of atomization of hydrazine, N_2H_4:

$$\begin{array}{c} H \\ {}^{\diagdown} \\ H \end{array} N-N \begin{array}{c} H \\ {}^{\diagup} \\ H \end{array} (g) \rightarrow 2\ N(g) + 4\ H(g),$$

for which $\Delta H^0 = +412$ kcal./mole. Hence

$$\bar{D}_{N-N}+4\ \bar{D}_{N-H} = 412 \text{ kcal.}$$

If it is again assumed that $\bar{D}_{N-H} = 93.4$ kcal./mole, then $\bar{D}_{N-N} = 38.4$ kcal./mole.

The heat of formation of tetrazan from its atoms (Δh_3) can now be assessed approximately as

$$\Delta h_3 = -(3\,\bar{D}_{N-N}+6\,\bar{D}_{N-H})$$
$$= -(115.2+560.4) = -675.6 \text{ kcal./mole}$$

and the standard heat of formation (from its elements) is

$$\Delta H_f^0 = \Delta h_1 + \Delta h_2 + \Delta h_3$$
$$= (4 \times 113.0) + (6 \times 52.09) + (-675.6)$$
$$= +88.9 \text{ kcal./mole}$$

The formation of tetrazan from its elements is thus likely to be a highly endothermic process. Furthermore, the entropy change is likely to be unfavorable also, since the reaction involves the formation of only one molecule from five reactant molecules in the gas phase. Such a process must lead to a decrease in the randomness of the system, and hence to a decrease in the entropy. Tetrazan is considered further in Chapter 3.

Mean thermochemical bond energies should be used for the above type of calculation only with considerable care. An example of the dangers inherent in the procedure follows.

Suppose it is desired to estimate the heat of formation of the unknown arsenic (V) chloride, $AsCl_5$, from the trichloride and chlorine, i.e., ΔH^0 for the reaction

$$AsCl_3\,(l) + Cl_2\,(g) \rightarrow AsCl_5\,(l) \tag{10}$$

From the reaction sequence

$$
\begin{array}{ll}
AsCl_3\,(l) \rightarrow AsCl_3\,(g) & \Delta h_1 \\
Cl_2\,(g) \rightarrow 2\;Cl\,(g) & \Delta h_2 \\
AsCl_3\,(g) + 2\;Cl\,(g) \rightarrow AsCl_5\,(g) & \Delta h_3 \\
AsCl_5\,(g) \rightarrow AsCl_5\,(l) & \Delta h_4
\end{array}
$$

it may be assumed, as a first approximation, that if $AsCl_5$ is a nonassociated liquid like $AsCl_3$, then Δh_1 and Δh_4 will roughly cancel each other. The heat of atomization of Cl_2, Δh_2, $= +58.0$ kcal./mole of Cl_2. The remaining term is Δh_3, and it is tempting to assume that the heat evolved in forming the two additional As—Cl covalent bonds is equal to twice

$\bar{D}_{As-Cl}$ ($= 2 \times -68.9 = -137.8$ kcal.) so that ΔH^0 for reaction (10) is approximately $-137.8 + 58.0 = -79.8$ kcal./mole.

However, the assumption that the two additional As—Cl bonds in $AsCl_5$ have the same bond energy as those in $AsCl_3$ (from which $\bar{D}_{As-Cl}$ is derived) is unlikely to be justified; in the comparable reaction

$$PCl_3(g) + 2\ Cl(g) \rightarrow PCl_5(g)$$

$\Delta H^0 = -80.1$ kcal./mole, i.e., the mean bond energy of the two additional P—Cl bonds is about 40 kcal., which is barely half of the mean energy of the three P—Cl bonds in PCl_3 (79.1 kcal.). Indeed, the fact that $AsCl_5$ has never been prepared (see Chapter 6) suggests that in this case the two extra As—Cl bonds are so weak that their heat of formation is insufficient to outweigh the heat absorbed in the atomization of the Cl_2 molecule, with the result that $AsCl_5$ is thermodynamically unstable with respect to $AsCl_3$ and Cl_2.

Estimation of ΔH_f^0 by Pauling's Empirical Procedure. A well-known empirical method for roughly estimating heats of formation is that due to Pauling (2). The fundamental postulate of this procedure is that, for a single covalent bond between two atoms A and B which differ in electronegativity, the energy $\bar{D}_{A-B}$ of the bond A—B is greater than the arithmetic mean of the energies $\bar{D}_{A-A}$ and $\bar{D}_{B-B}$ by an amount Δ, which is a measure of the extent to which the bond A—B is stabilized by ionic-covalent resonance:

$$\Delta = \bar{D}_{A-B} - \tfrac{1}{2}(\bar{D}_{A-A} + \bar{D}_{B-B}) \qquad (11)$$

Electronegativity coefficients X_A and X_B were then assigned to A and B, such that

$$|X_A - X_B| = (\Delta/23)^{\frac{1}{2}} \qquad (12)$$

The well-known Pauling electronegativity coefficients (X) for the elements are given in Table 1.10. From (11) and (12), it follows that

$$\bar{D}_{A-B} = \tfrac{1}{2}(\bar{D}_{A-A} + \bar{D}_{B-B}) + 23|X_A - X_B|^2$$

If A and B have identical electronegativities then there is no ionic-covalent resonance stabilization of the bond A—B, and

$$\bar{D}_{A-B} = \tfrac{1}{2}(\bar{D}_{A-A} + \bar{D}_{B-B})$$

This is the case for sulphur and iodine, for both of which $X = 2.5$.

Table 1.10

Electronegativity Coefficients (2)

(The coefficients refer to the common oxidation states of the elements.)

Li	Be	B												C	N	O	F
1.0	1.5	2.0												2.5	3.0	3.5	4.0
Na	Mg	Al												Si	P	S	Cl
0.9	1.2	1.5												1.8	2.1	2.5	3.0
K	Ca	Sc	Ti	V	Cr	Mn	Fe	Co	Ni	Cu	Zn	Ga	Ge	As	Se	Br
0.8	1.0	1.3	1.5	1.6	1.6	1.5	1.8	1.8	1.8	1.9	1.6	1.6	1.8	2.0	2.4	2.8
Rb	Sr	Y	Zr	Nb	Mo	Tc	Ru	Rh	Pd	Ag	Cd	In	Sn	Sb	Te	I
0.8	1.0	1.2	1.4	1.6	1.8	1.9	2.2	2.2	2.2	1.9	1.7	1.7	1.8	1.9	2.1	2.5
Cs	Ba	La	Hf	Ta	W	Re	Os	Ir	Pt	Au	Hg	Tl	Pb	Bi	Po	At
0.7	0.9	1.1	1.3	1.5	1.7	1.9	2.2	2.2	2.2	2.4	1.9	1.8	1.8	1.9	2.0	2.2
Fr	Ra	Ac	Th	Pa	U											
0.7	0.9	1.1	1.3	1.5	1.7											

Hence for the gas phase formation of a molecule such as SI_2 from its single-bonded elements S_8 and I_2, viz.,

$$\tfrac{1}{8}\, S_8(g) + I_2(g) \rightarrow SI_2(g)$$

one would expect ΔH^0 to be zero.

For cases in which $X_A \neq X_B$, the heat of formation of gas phase molecules from single-bonded gaseous elements would be greater (in the negative sense) than zero by an amount $23|X_A - X_B|^2$ for each bond in the molecule. Thus, heats of formation may be estimated from Pauling's electronegativity coefficients, but corrections must be made (a) if the standard states of either the elements or the resulting compound are not gaseous, and (b) if the elements are not single-bonded, as is the case with nitrogen and oxygen. The method makes no allowance for variation of electronegativity with oxidation state, and is subject to the same rather severe limitations which arise from the use of mean bond energies.

An estimate of the heat of formation of the unknown compound nitrogen tri-iodide, NI_3, assuming it to be a solid in its standard state and using Pauling's procedure, is given below.

Consider first the enthalpy change for the gas phase reaction

$$\tfrac{1}{2}\, N_2(g) + 1\tfrac{1}{2}\, I_2(g) \rightarrow NI_3(g) \tag{13}$$

Since $X_N = 3.0$ and $X_I = 2.5$, then NI_3 is more stable than its *single bonded* elements by 23 $(3.0-2.5)^2 = 5.75$ kcal. for each of the three N—I bonds, or $3 \times 5.75 = 17.3$ kcal./mole in total. But the element N_2 is not single bonded, and its triple $N \equiv N$ bond is considerably more stable than three single N—N bonds by the amount $\bar{D}_{N \equiv N} - 3\bar{D}_{N-N} = 226 - (3 \times 38.4) = 110.8$ kcal./mole of N_2, or 55.4 kcal./mole of N atoms. The ionic-covalent resonance stabilization of NI_3 (17.3 kcal./mole) is thus not sufficient to outweigh the extra stability of the triple bond in N_2 (55.4 kcal./mole of N atoms), and the estimated enthalpy change for reaction (13) is thus

$$\Delta H^0 = -17.3 + 55.4 = +38.1 \text{ kcal./mole}$$

For the standard heat of formation ΔH_f^0 of NI_3, however, we require the enthalpy change for the reaction in which reactants and products are in their standard states, viz.,

$$\tfrac{1}{2} N_2(g) + 1\tfrac{1}{2} I_2(s) \rightarrow NI_3(s)$$

Therefore, ΔH^0 for reaction (8) should be corrected for the heats of sublimation of $I_2(s)$ and $NI_3(s)$. As an approximation it may be assumed that the van der Waals forces between I_2 molecules in solid iodine are of the same order of magnitude as those between NI_3 molecules in solid nitrogen tri-iodide, and that this correction may be ignored. The estimated standard heat of formation ΔH_f^0 is thus about $+38$ kcal./mole, i.e., the compound is expected to be thermodynamically unstable with respect to its elements. The results of this sort of calculation for all four nitrogen trihalides are as follows:

	ΔH_f^0 (estimated)	ΔH_f^0 (kcal./mole) (experimental)
NF_3	-13.6	-27.2
NCl_3	$+55.4$	$+54.7$
NBr_3	$+52.6$	$-$
NI_3	$+38.1$	$-$

Only the trifluoride is thermodynamically stable with respect to its elements; the highly endothermic nature of the other trihalides parallels their observed instability.

From the foregoing discussion it is clear that the methods available

for estimating the thermodynamic quantities required to predict the energetic feasibility of a reaction are often crude. Even greater difficulties
may be encountered in predicting reaction rates. In the pages which follow, it has seldom been found possible to attempt even an approximate
evaluation of the desired thermodynamic quantities, and recourse has been
had to qualitative arguments; it is hoped nevertheless that the search for
an answer to the question "why has compound X never been prepared?"
may prove both profitable and stimulating, and that it will provide a
healthy source of recognition of the very limited nature of our understand-
ing, at a quantitative level, of the factors influencing chemical reactivity.

REFERENCES

(1) Latimer, W. M., *Oxidation Potentials*, 2nd ed., Prentice-Hall, Inc.,
    New York, 1952, p. 359.
(2) Pauling, L., *The Nature of the Chemical Bond*, 3rd ed., Cornell University
    Press, New York, 1960.
(3) Lewis, G. N., and M. Randall, *Thermodynamics*, revised by K. S. Pitzer
    and L. Brewer, 2nd ed., McGraw-Hill, New York, 1961.
(4) Davis, W. D., L. S. Mason, and G. Stegeman, *J. Am. Chem. Soc.*, **71**,
    2775, (1949).
(5) Altshuller, A. P., *J. Chem. Phys.*, **22**, 1136 (1954).
(6) Waddington, T. C., in H. J. Emeleus and A. G. Sharpe, eds., *Advances in
    Inorganic Chemistry and Radiochemistry*, Vol. 1, Academic Press, Inc.,
    New York, 1959, p. 158.
(7) Born, M., and A. Lande, *Verhandl. deut. Ges. Physik.*, **20**, 210 (1918).
(8) Born, M., and J. E. Mayer, *Z. Physik*, **75**, 1 (1932).
(9) Cotton, F. A., and G. Wilkinson, *Advanced Inorganic Chemistry*, Inter-
    science, New York, 1962, p. 44.
(10) Kapustinskii, A. F., *Quart. Rev. (London)*, **10**, 283 (1956).
(11) Yatsimirskii, K. B., *Izv. Akad. Nauk SSSR, Otd. Khim. Nauk*, 453 (1947);
    398 (1948); A. F. Kapustinskii and K. B. Yatsimirskii, *Zh. Obshch. Khim.*,
    19, 2191 (1949). See ref. (10).
(12) Barber, M., J. W. Linnett, and N. H. Taylor, *J. Chem. Soc.*, **1961**, 3323.
(13) Orgel, L. E., *Proc. 10th. Solvay Conf. Chem., Brussels*, 289 (1956).
(14) Hush, N. S., and M. N. L. Pryce, *J. Chem. Phys.*, **28**, 244 (1958).
(15) Yatsimirskii, K. B., *Russ. J. Inorg. Chem., (English Transl.)* **6**, 265 (1961).
(16) Grimm, H. G., and K. F. Herzfeld, *Z. Physik*, **19**, 141 (1923).
(17) Waddington, T. C., *Trans. Faraday Soc.*, **55**, 1531 (1959).
(18) Ladd, M. F. C., and W. H. Lee, *Trans. Faraday Soc.*, **54**, 4 (1958).
(19) Garrick, F. J., *Phil. Mag.*, **9**, 131 (1930); **10**, 71, 76 (1930); **11**, 741 (1931);
    14, 914 (1932).

(20) Basolo, F., and R. G. Pearson, *Mechanisms of Inorganic Reactions*, John Wiley and Sons, Inc., New York, 1958, p. 46.

(21) Van Arkel, A. E., and J. H. De Boer, *Die Chemische Bindung als elektrostatische Erscheinung*, Hirzel, Leipzig, 1931.

(22) Mortimer, C. T., *Reaction Heats and Bond Strengths*, Pergamon Press, New York, 1962.

(23) Cotton, F. A., and J. R. Leto, *J. Chem. Phys.*, **30**, 993 (1959).

(24) Skinner, H. A., *Ann. Rept. Progr. Chem. (Chem. Soc. London)* **57**, 21 (1960)

(25) Kubaschewski, O., and E. L. Evans, *Metallurgical Thermochemistry*, Pergamon Press, London, 1956, p. 194.

(26) Moody, G. J., and J. D. R. Thomas, *J. Chem. Soc.*, **1964**, 1417.

(27) Petrakis, L., *J. Phys. Chem.*, **66,** 433 (1962).

Chapter 2

Compounds Whose Instability is a Consequence of the Restriction of First-Row Atoms (Li to F) to a Valence Octet

I. GENERAL

In spite of the stability of a valence-shell octet of electrons, it is well-known that elements of the second and subsequent rows of the periodic table may form compounds which, when formulated with two-electron bonds, involve more than eight valence-shell electrons; such an element (e.g., Si, P, S) is sometimes said to "expand its octet." That the first-row elements, from lithium to fluorine, are rigorously restricted to an octet of valence electrons was recognized by Sidgwick (1, 2), who assigned a "maximum covalency" of four to the elements of the first short period. Apparently as a result of this restriction, there are many compounds of first-row atoms which have never been prepared, for example,

$$Na_3BF_6 \qquad Na_2CF_6 \qquad NF_5 \qquad OF_4$$
$$K_3B(C_2O_4)_3 \qquad \qquad NaNF_6 \qquad OF_6$$

whereas their second-row analogues are well-known and relatively stable:

$$Na_3AlF_6 \qquad Na_2SiF_6 \qquad PF_5 \qquad SF_4$$
$$K_3Al(C_2O_4)_3 \qquad \qquad NaPF_6 \qquad SF_6$$

The early literature contains numerous accounts of the unsuccessful efforts made to prepare the missing first-row compounds. For example, Hildebrand, Merrill, and Simons (3) described attempts to synthesize a salt of the carbon analogue (H_2CF_6) of fluorosilicic acid (H_2SiF_6), by condensing carbon tetrafluoride on cesium fluoride at $-80°C.$, in the hope

35

that the reaction

$$CF_4 + 2\,CsF \rightarrow Cs_2CF_6$$

might proceed. No reaction ensued. Similarly, a study of the time/temperature curve obtained when a mixture of carbon tetrafluoride and hydrogen fluoride was allowed to warm slowly showed that breaks in the curve occurred only at the freezing points of the constituents.

The octet limitation appears to be a consequence of the electron configurations of the first-row atoms, which can accommodate a maximum of eight electrons in the $2s$ and $2p$ orbitals. Formation of more than four two-electron covalent bonds by these atoms would necessitate the use of their $3d$ orbitals, and the energy difference between these and the orbitals of the preceding quantum level is so large as to make the promotional energies involved in their use excessively high.

A comparison of the electronic energy levels of a first-row atom (nitrogen) with its second-row analogue (phosphorus) is shown in Figure 2.1. The data upon which the figure is based are only rough approximations calculated from spectroscopic data (4) by the method of Jaffé (5); furthermore the levels refer to pure (i.e., unhybridized) atomic orbitals, whereas in the compounds considered hybrid orbitals are likely to be used. Nevertheless the data are useful for comparative purposes.

In order that nitrogen or phosphorus may form five-covalent molecules NX_5 and PX_5, it is necessary first to uncouple the valence-shell s^2 electron pair and to promote one of the electrons to the available $3d$ orbital of lowest energy. It can be seen from Figure 2.1 that the promotion energies are

$$N(2s^2\,2p^3) \rightarrow N(2s^1\,2p^3\,3d^1) \qquad 18.9 \text{ e.v.}$$

and

$$P(3s^2\,3p^3) \rightarrow P(3s^1\,3p^3\,3d^1) \qquad 14.4 \text{ e.v.}$$

The promotion energy necessary is thus about 4.5 e.v. (say 100 kcal./mole) higher for nitrogen than for phosphorus, and this big energy difference seems to be the major factor precluding the formation of nitrogen analogues of PF_5, PCl_5, and PBr_5.

Gillespie (6) has argued that first-row atoms such as carbon and nitrogen may indeed use their $3d$ orbitals in bonding; his argument (which has been criticized (7)) is based on the assertion that the $3s \rightarrow 3d$ promotion energy

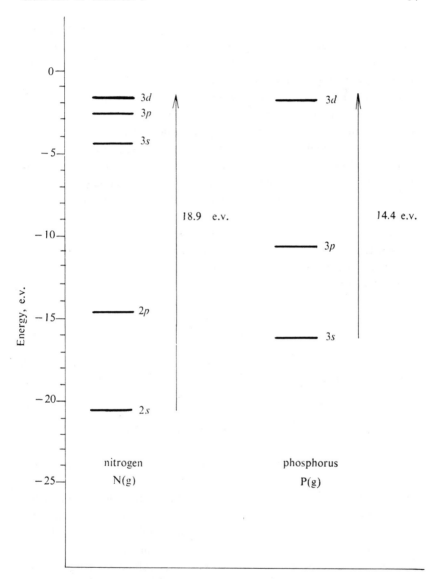

Figure 2.1. Energy levels of N and P atomic orbitals.

required even for phosphorus ($\sim$ 14 e.v.) is too high to be adequately offset by the energy of formation of the additional covalent bonds, and that the actual promotion energy involved must be substantially less than

14 e.v. Gillespie believes that electronegative ligands such as F, Cl, and Br must lower the energy of the phosphorus $3d$ orbitals (or hybrid orbitals with a proportion of $3d$ character) quite substantially, and that a corresponding lowering might be possible for nitrogen and other first-row atoms.

On the other hand, it must be acknowledged that there is still some dispute concerning whether or not $3d$ orbitals are used even by second-row elements like phosphorus in its pentahalides. Hudson (14) reviewed the theoretical treatments of PX_5 molecules and concluded that the importance of sigma-bonding $3d$ orbitals in phosphorus chemistry is probably very small. He considered, in agreement with Gillespie, that the $3s \rightarrow 3d$ promotion energy is excessively high, but that (contrary to Gillespie) the promotion energy is increased rather than decreased by the perturbing effect of electronegative ligands. If this is the case, then the nonexistence of NCl_5 and similar compounds must be attributed to the instability (arising from the high electronegativity of nitrogen) of valence-bond structures like

$$\begin{array}{ccc}
Cl & \overset{\textstyle Cl}{\underset{\textstyle |}{}} & Cl^- \\
\diagdown & & \\
& N^+ & \\
\diagup & \diagdown & \\
Cl & & Cl \\
\end{array}$$

which must be invoked in order to formulate a 5-covalent molecule without recourse to $3d$ orbitals, i.e., without "expanding the octet."

II. OXYACIDS OF FLUORINE

The three halogens chlorine, bromine, and iodine all form several oxyacids. In contrast, there is no well-established example of any oxyacid, or salt of an oxyacid, of the lightest halogen, fluorine. This fact is almost certainly related to the octet restriction on first-row elements. The only evidence for the formation of an oxyacid of fluorine was obtained by Dennis and Rochow (8), who obtained, by the fluorination of 50 % potassium hydroxide solution at $-80°C$. a white solid possessing oxidizing properties which persisted even after fusion. It was considered that the white solid might contain either a hypofluorite (KFO) or a fluorate (KFO_3). However Cady, who repeated the experiment (9), considered it more likely that the product contained a salt of an oxyacid of chlorine, formed from chloride ion initially present as an impurity in the potassium hydroxide. In another experiment, Dennis and Rochow (8) electrolyzed a mixture of fused potassium hydroxide and potassium fluoride and obtained a product which, after solution in water and precipitation with silver nitrate solution, gave a white solid which was insoluble in nitric acid. X-ray examination of the solid showed that although part of it was silver chloride, the remainder consisted of tetragonal crystals which were considered to be silver fluorate, $AgFO_3$. Although Ruff (10) has expressed the view that the product has the (improbable) formula $AgOF_3$, this work does not seem to have been re-investigated. However, theoretical considerations which are outlined in the following paragraph suggest strongly that a fluorate is unlikely to exist.

The conventional single-bonded formulation of an ion such as FO_4^- is as follows,

$$
\begin{array}{ccc}
^{-}O & & O^{-} \\
& \!\!\!\!\diagdown\, ^{3+}\! \diagup & \\
& F & \\
& \diagup \quad \diagdown & \\
^{-}O & & O^{-}
\end{array}
$$

in which the charges shown are formal, i.e., they are those which would exist if the bonding electron pairs were shared equally between the fluorine and oxygen atoms. This is not of course the case since fluorine, which is uniquely more electronegative than oxygen, would attract any bonding electrons more strongly and thus reduce somewhat the positive charge on the central F atom. Inevitably however the F atom in such a single bonded structure must be to some extent positively charged with respect to the oxygen, and Wells (11) has pointed out that such a structure must be inherently unstable in view of the electronegativity relationship between fluorine and oxygen. In similar but stable ions formed by the other halogens, e.g., ClO_4^-, the oxygen atom has the higher electronegativity and the difficulty of the positive charge on the central halogen atom is not so apparent. Nevertheless, in oxyanions such as ClO_4^-, there is abundant evidence (12) that the Cl—O bond is not a single electron-pair bond, but has stabilizing multiple-bond character resulting from the back coordination of the lone pair p_π orbitals of the oxygen atoms into the vacant $3d$ orbitals of the chlorine atom. This has the effect of reducing the accumulation of positive charge on the halogen atom, but the significant fact is that multiple bonding of this sort cannot occur where the halogen atom is fluorine, because of its lack of $3d$ orbitals of suitably low energy.

This fact has been considered (13) of major importance in assessing the reasons for the apparent nonexistence of fluorine oxyacids.

The only case where the difficulty of positively-charged fluorine is absent appears to be molecular hypofluorous acid, H—O—F. It seems at least possible that this compound could exist, though it has not been identified among the hydrolysis products of F_2O.

REFERENCES

(1) Sidgwick, N. V., *The Electronic Theory of Valency*, Oxford University Press, London, 1927, Chapter 9.
(2) Sidgwick, N. V., *Trans. Faraday Soc.*, **19**, 469 (1923).
(3) Hildebrand, J. H., H. B. Merrill, and J. Simons, *J. Am. Chem. Soc.*, **46**, 2225 (1924).
(4) Moore, C. E., "*Atomic Energy Levels*", Nat. Bur. Std. (*U.S.*), Circ. 467, (1949).
(5) Jaffé, H. H., *J. Chem. Educ.*, **33**, 25 (1956).
(6) Gillespie, R. J., *J. Chem. Soc.*, **1952**, 1002, *J. Chem. Phys.*, **21**, 1893 (1953).
(7) Jaffé, H. H., *J. Chem. Phys.*, **24**, 1893 (1953).
(8) Dennis, L. M., and E. G. Rochow, *J. Am. Chem. Soc.*, **54**, 832 (1932); **55**, 2431 (1933).
(9) Cady, G. H., *J. Am. Chem. Soc.*, **56**, 1647 (1934).
(10) Ruff, O., *Ber.*, **69(A)**, 181 (1936).
(11) Wells, A. F., *J. Chem. Soc.*, **1949**, 63.
(12) Cruickshank, D. W. J., *J. Chem. Soc.*, **1961**, 5486.
(13) Phillips, G. M., J. S. Hunter, and L. E. Sutton, *J. Chem. Soc.*, **1945**, 146.
(14) Hudson, R. F., in H. J. Emeleus and A. G. Sharpe, eds., *Advances in Inorganic Chemistry and Radiochemistry*, Vol. 5, Academic Press, Inc., New York, 1963, p. 351.

Chapter 3

Compounds Whose Instability is Related to the Reluctance of Certain Atoms to Undergo Self-Linkage or Catenation

I. GENERAL

The carbon atom is unexcelled in its capacity for forming covalent bonds with itself, and the emergence of organic chemistry as one of the major chemical disciplines is of course related to the great diversity of compounds containing C to C bonds. Other atoms in the same periodic group as carbon show this capacity (called catenation) to a much lesser extent, and the tendency to form X—X covalent bonds appears to decrease down the group C-Si-Ge-Sn-Pb. Although catenation in the second-row element silicon is much less widespread than in carbon, precisely the reverse situation is observed in the pairs of elements nitrogen and phosphorus, and oxygen and sulfur, where the second-row atoms (P and S) undergo self-linkage to a much greater extent than their first-row congeners (N and O). Thus there are no nitrogen analogues of P_4 or red or black phosphorus, nor oxygen analogues of S_8, polysulfides, and so on.

In this chapter the fairly regular trend away from catenation in group 4 is examined first, and the fifth and sixth periodic groups subsequently.

II. CATENATION IN C, Si, Ge, Sn, AND Pb

A. Silicon

Compounds containing Si—Si bonds which have been isolated and

fully characterized both chemically and structurally are still comparatively few in number. They comprise mainly the compounds $Si_n X_{2n+2}$,
where X = H, halogen, or organic radical; only where n is small (usually 2 or 3) are the compounds at all well-known. There is however a
substantial literature dealing with imperfectly-characterized substances
whose formulas imply the presence of Si—Si bonds. It seems that Si—Si
catenation may be more widespread than is usually thought to be the
case, particularly in view of the development of quite an extensive chemistry of organo-derivatives.

A vapor-phase chromatographic study (1) of the products of the acid
hydrolysis of magnesium silicide revealed the existence of twenty-one silicon hydrides or *silanes*, the highest member of which was tentatively
identified as $n\text{-}Si_8H_{18}$. Only the lower members have been studied in any
detail (2, 3).

Quite extensive Si—Si bonding appears to be involved in some chlor-
inated silanes, such as Si_5Cl_{12}(4), for which a neo-pentyl structure
has been suggested, and Si_6Cl_{14}(5). The remarkable, highly viscous
derivatives $Si_{10}Cl_{22}$ and $Si_{25}Cl_{52}$(6) have not been subjected to any
precise structural investigation, nor have $Si_{10}Cl_{20}H_2$ and $Si_{10}Cl_{18}$, although the last compound is claimed to be an analogue of decalin, with
the bicyclic structure

Recent developments in the chemistry of perchloropolysilanes have
been summarized (103).

Extensive Si—Si bonding is apparently involved in the numerous
"subcompounds" of silicon, which are extensively polymerized, amorphous substances commonly obtained by thermal or electrical decomposition of simple molecular compounds. These subhydrides, subhalides,
etcetera are usually colored (although some of them are white), and

have so far defied any rigorous structural investigation. Examples are collected in Table 3.1. Typical are the hydrides which have compositions ranging from $SiH_{0.4}$ to SiH_2; they are all yellow or brown nonvolatile solids which are amorphous to X-rays, and are presumably highly

Table 3.1

Polymeric Silicon Compounds in Which Si—Si Bonding is Apparently Involved

Hydrides		References
$(SiH_{0.4-0.9})_x$	brown powder	(8,9)
$(SiH_{1.1-1.6})_x$	yellow solid	(10)
$(SiH_{1.2-1.7})_x$	brown powder	(11)
$(SiH)_x$	yellow solid	(12)
$(SiH_2)_x$	light brown powder	(11,13)
Halides		
$(SiF_n)_x$	yellow powder	(14)
$(SiCl)_x$	red solid	(15,16)
$(SiCl_{1-2})_x$	viscous liquids	(7)
$(SiBr_{1-2})_x$	brown solids	(13)
$(SiBr)_x$	brown-yellow solid	(16)
$(SiI)_x$	orange-red solid	(17)
Organic Derivatives		
$[Si(CH_3)_2]_x$	white solid	(18)
$(SiR_2)_x$,	viscous oils	(13)
$R = CH_3,\ CH_3CH_2,$		
$C_3H_7,\ C_4H_9$		
$(SiPh_2)_x$	resin	(22)
Oxygen Derivatives		
$(Si_2H_2O)_x$ (siloxene)	white solid	(19,20)
$(Si_6H_4O_9)_x$	yellow solid	(21)
$(Si_6H_2O_9)_x$	orange solid	(21)
$(Si_6O_9)_x$	golden-brown solid	(21)

polymerized substances involving random networks of Si—Si bonds with sufficient Si—H bonds to satisfy the tetravalence of silicon.

There is an extensive chemistry of organic derivatives of silicon, in which catenated compounds are fairly abundant, particularly among the phenyl compounds; the classical work in this field is that of F. S. Kipping, and it has been reviewed, along with recent developments, by Ingham and Gilman (86). Some typical compounds are as follows:

1,4-diiodooctaphenyltetrasilane (87)

$$I-\underset{\underset{R}{|}}{\overset{\overset{R}{|}}{Si}}-\underset{\underset{R}{|}}{\overset{\overset{R}{|}}{Si}}-\underset{\underset{R}{|}}{\overset{\overset{R}{|}}{Si}}-\underset{\underset{R}{|}}{\overset{\overset{R}{|}}{Si}}-I, \qquad R=C_6H_5$$

1,5-dihydroxydecaphenylpentasilane (88)

$$HO-\underset{\underset{R}{|}}{\overset{\overset{R}{|}}{Si}}-\underset{\underset{R}{|}}{\overset{\overset{R}{|}}{Si}}-\underset{\underset{R}{|}}{\overset{\overset{R}{|}}{Si}}-\underset{\underset{R}{|}}{\overset{\overset{R}{|}}{Si}}-\underset{\underset{R}{|}}{\overset{\overset{R}{|}}{Si}}-OH, \qquad R=C_6H_5$$

decaphenylcyclopentasilane (89)

$$\begin{array}{c} R_2Si-SiR_2 \\ | \qquad | \\ R_2Si \qquad SiR_2 \; , \; R=C_6H_5 \\ \diagdown \diagup \\ SiR_2 \end{array}$$

octaphenylcyclotetrasilane (87)

$$\begin{array}{c} R_2Si-SiR_2 \\ | \qquad | \\ R_2Si-SiR_2 \end{array} \; , \; R=C_6H_5$$

The apparent stabilization of Si—Si bonds by the aromatic phenyl substituent (an effect also apparent in Ge—Ge and Sn—Sn compounds: see Section II B) suggests some significant interaction between the π-orbitals of the phenyl groups and those of the $-Si_n-$ system; an intense band in the ultraviolet spectrum of such compounds may arise from such an interaction (102).

The oxygenated compound siloxene, $(Si_2H_2O)_x$, and its numerous derivatives formed by substitution of the hydrogen atoms, have been extensively studied (19) by Kautsky, who has suggested that siloxene has a two-dimensional layer structure based upon the repeating unit

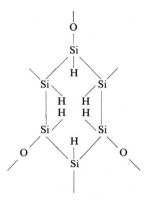

That the number of simple catenated molecules that have been fully characterized is still comparatively small would appear to be due to a number of factors, mainly of a preparative and manipulative nature. Some of these are:

(a) Many of the classical methods for ascending a *carbon* series are not available in silicon chemistry because of the nonexistence of the corresponding reagents. Some common methods for adding a carbon atom to an organic compound are as follows:

(i) alkyl halide + potassium cyanide,

$$R-X+KCN \rightarrow R-CN+KX$$

(ii) acid chloride + diazomethane (Arndt-Eistert reaction),

$$RCOCl+2\,CH_2N_2 \rightarrow RCOCHN_2+CH_3Cl+N_2$$
$$RCOCHN_2+H_2O \rightarrow RCH_2COOH+N_2$$

(iii) Grignard reagent + CO_2, or + formaldehyde

$$RMgX+CO_2 \rightarrow RCOOMgX \xrightarrow{H_2O} RCOOH$$
$$RMgX+HCHO \rightarrow RCH_2OMgX \xrightarrow{H_2O} RCH_2OH$$

Equivalent methods for lengthening a silicon chain are not feasible because in (i) there are no silicon analogues of the cyanides, $R-Si\equiv N$; in (ii) there are no compounds containing the equivalent of a carbonyl group, such as

$$R-Si\underset{Cl}{\overset{O}{\diagup}}$$

and in (iii) silicon dioxide, unlike carbon dioxide, is an unreactive polymerized compound, and again the silicon analogue of formaldehyde contains no $Si=O$ group.

However, recent use has been made of organosilyl compounds (22) to synthesize molecules containing branched Si—Si chains.

(b) Polymerization of silicon compounds usually proceeds uncontrollably as soon as the appropriate unit (e.g., SiH_2) has been formed, whereas the corresponding processes with carbon compounds are more manageable and normally require a catalyst.

(c) Preparative difficulties are exacerbated by the proneness of the silicon atom to chemical attack. In silicon compounds the bonds present may not differ much in strength when compared with those in the carbon analogues, but because the Si atom possesses a vacant set of energetically accessible $3d$ orbitals, the formation of polycovalent transition states with attacking molecules or ions is greatly facilitated.

(d) The possibility that the Si—Si bond is intrinsically weak is discussed subsequently (Section II C of this chapter).

B. Germanium, Tin, Lead

Reported compounds containing Ge—Ge bonds are comparatively few except in the case of the hydrides (germanes), where an extensive series up to Ge_9H_{20} has been obtained (26). Catenation in germanium compounds is distinctly less widespread than is the case in silicon chemistry. An interesting development has been the preparation of mixed hydrides containing Ge−Si bonds (104).

There is a small group of apparently polymeric subcompounds such as $(GeH)_x$ (27, 28, 29, 30, 31), $(GeH_2)_x$ (31, 32, 33), $(GeCl)_x$ (34, 35), and $(GeF)_x$ (36).

It is probable that the dihalides GeX_2 contain a Ge species with two valence electrons in an unreactive condition (the so-called "inert pair") rather than Ge—Ge bonds; this has been established for the di-iodide GeI_2, in which the germanium atoms are surrounded by octahedra of equidistant iodine atoms (37), and the low melting point (110°C.), solubility, and ready volatility of the difluoride GeF_2 (36) do not support the presence of a polymeric, Ge—Ge bonded structure.

Although Ge_2Cl_6 appears to be the only polynuclear halide, a few organic derivatives have compositions which suggest more extensive

Ge—Ge bonding, e.g., $(Ph_2Ge)_4$, (38) and $(PhGe)_6$ (39), although the last compound contains some oxygen (40). More highly polymerized aryl derivatives have been described by Glockling and Hooton (41).

A further decrease in catenation is observed in passing from germanium to tin. Thus, the only recorded hydride apart from SnH_4 itself is the very unstable distannane, Sn_2H_6 (42), and polynuclear halides appear to be nonexistent. The most extensively catenated tin compounds are found among the organic derivatives, in which up to five Sn—Sn bonds are apparently formed, e.g., $(CH_3)_8Sn_3$(43), $(CH_3)_{10}Sn_4$(44), $(CH_3)_{12}Sn_5$ (43), and $Ph_{12}Sn_5$(108).

In tin, the "inert pair effect" is well-established and many substances with formula R_2Sn are genuine divalent compounds; there are however a number of polymeric organic derivatives (R = alkyl or aryl) which evidently contain Sn—Sn bonds (43, 45, 46, 106). These are usually yellow, insoluble polymerized solids, but in a few cases, e.g., Ph_2Sn(47), a monomer exists which only slowly polymerizes on standing. Possible modes of bonding in this diphenyl derivative, which has a dipole moment close to to 1.0 D at all stages of polymerization, have been suggested (45, 47). An X-ray examination of the diphenyl derivative has established the presence of a six-fold polymer containing a six-membered ring of Sn atoms (105).

In the final member of the group, lead, catenation has almost disappeared, and is confined to a small group of organic derivatives containing a single Pb—Pb bond, such as $(CH_3)_3Pb$—$Pb(CH_3)_3$ (48).

C. Strengths of the X—X Bonds (X = C, Si, Ge, Sn, Pb)

The decrease in catenation observed in passing from carbon to lead has been commonly attributed to a decrease in the strength of the covalent bonds from C—C to Pb—Pb; such a decrease can be related to the increasing diffuseness of the atomic orbitals in passing down the group, giving rise to a concomitant poorer overlap, and lower bond strength, on homopolar covalent bond formation. A simple example of such a trend within a periodic group is observed in the diatomic molecules formed to a small extent in the gas phase by the alkali metals, Li, Na, K, Rb, and Cs. These molecules contain a single covalent bond of the sigma type, formed by overlap of singly-occupied s orbitals in the valence shell of the alkali metal atoms, and the bond-dissociation energy D_{M-M}

decreases from lithium to cesium:

	D_{M-M}, kcal./mole (25)
Li—Li	25
Na—Na	17.3
K—K	11.8
Rb—Rb	10.8
Cs—Cs	10.4

Pauling (24) calculated C—C, Si—Si, Ge—Ge, and Sn—Sn mean thermochemical bond energies from the heats of atomization of diamond, silicon, germanium, and tin, all of which have the diamond structure, as follows:

	$\bar{D}_{X-X}$, kcal./mole
C—C	83.1
Si—Si	42.2
Ge—Ge	37.6
Sn—Sn	34.2

These values show the same trend as the alkali metal series, and establish that the Si—Si bond in elementary silicon is much weaker than the C—C bond in diamond, and that the Ge—Ge and Sn—Sn bonds are weaker still.

The value of the C—C bond energy (83.1 kcal./mole) is very similar to the C—C bond-dissociation energy of ethane, i.e., the change in energy accompanying the gas-phase process

$$CH_3\text{—}CH_3 \rightarrow 2\ CH_3$$

which has been found (25) to be 83 kcal./mole.

Thermochemical bond energies for these bonds have also been obtained from heats of dissociation of the hydrides M_2H_6 by Gunn and Green (26):

$\bar{D}_{C-C}$ (C_2H_6)	78.8 kcal./mole
$\bar{D}_{Si-Si}$ (Si_2H_6)	46.4
$\bar{D}_{Ge-Ge}$ (Ge_2H_6)	37.9

These figures, which depend on the assumption that the M—H bond energies are the same as those determined by decomposition of the mononuclear hydrides MH_4, are in the same relative order as those recorded by Pauling.

However, a more recent electron-impact study (23) of the bond-dissociation energies for the gas-phase process

$$R_3Si—SiR_3 \rightarrow 2\ SiR_3$$

where R = H and Cl, has given the values

$$D_{H_3Si-SiH_3} = 81.3\ kcal./mole$$

and

$$D_{Cl_3Si-SiCl_3} = 85\ kcal./mole$$

which imply that in these compounds the Si—Si bond is similar in strength to the C—C bond in ethane. From these data the curious fact emerges that the C—C bonds in diamond and ethane have about the same strength ($\sim$ 83 kcal./mole), while the Si—Si bonds in elementary silicon and disilane apparently differ by about 40 kcal. There is thus some uncertainty as to the relative strengths of C—C and Si—Si bonds, and the influence of this factor on Si—Si catenation is uncertain.

In this connection, it is interesting that Mulliken (81) has calculated overlap integrals for C—C and Si—Si covalent bonds. The overlap integral S is defined by the relationship

$$S = \int \psi_1 \cdot \psi_2\ dv$$

where ψ_1, ψ_2 are the atomic orbitals (usually the normalized Slater type) which overlap to form the bond considered, and dv is a small volume element; the integration extends over all space. For ψ_1 and ψ_2 Mulliken used tetrahedral (te) sp_3 hybrids and evaluated S for $te_\sigma - te_\sigma$ (sigma type) overlap at the measured internuclear distances. His results are

$$S_{C-C} = 0.65 \qquad S_{Si-Si} = 0.73$$

The overlap integral, which gives a measure of the concentration of electronic charge between the nuclei, is not an altogether satisfactory index of bond strength. Nevertheless the similar values obtained for the C—C and Si—Si bonds do suggest that the energies of these bonds may not differ very much.

The relatively low bond energies for Ge—Ge (37.6) and Sn—Sn (34.2) quoted by Pauling (24) have not so far been disputed, and it can be presumed that the comparative rarity of catenation in compounds of these elements, and of lead, is due in large measure to this circumstance.

III. CATENATION IN N, P, As, Sb, AND Bi

A. Nitrogen

In the group 5 sequence of elements —N, P, As, Sb, Bi— there is striking departure from the trend towards catenation observed in group 4, in that the top member of the group, nitrogen, shows only a very small tendency to form N—N bonds; in this respect it is inferior to phosphorus, for which a moderate degree of P—P bonding is discernable. This reluctance of nitrogen to form N—N single bonds is of course in very sharp contrast to the unexcelled C—C bonding capacity of carbon, the top member of group 4. Well-known compounds containing N—N bonds are restricted to hydrazine, $H_2N \cdot NH_2$, and its many derivatives; tetrazan (see Chapter 1, Section IIC), $H_2N \cdot NH \cdot NH \cdot NH_2$ (49) and its hexaphenyl derivative (50) are poorly-characterized compounds stable only at very low temperatures. The longest nitrogen chain known (51) occurs in the unstable, explosive substance

$$\phi{-}N = N{-}\underset{\phi}{N}{-}N = N{-}\underset{\phi}{N}{-}N = N{-}\phi, \qquad \phi = C_6H_5$$

although in the formula as written not all of the N—N bonds are single.

B. Phosphorus

By comparison catenation in phosphorus, although by no means widespread, is not as uncommon as is the case for nitrogen, and a summary of compounds containing P—P bonds will now be given.

1. Diphosphorus (P—P) Compounds. Apart from diphosphine, P_2H_4, compounds which contain two singly linked P atoms include $P_2(CH_3)_4$ (52); P_2Ph_4 (53);

$$\underset{CH_3}{\overset{CH_3CH_2}{\diagdown}}P{-}P\underset{CH_3}{\overset{CH_2CH_3}{\diagup}} \qquad (54)$$

and $P_2(CF_3)_4$ (55).

The oxyacid anions $HP_2O_5^{3-}$ (diphosphite) and $P_2O_6^{3-}$ (hypophosphate) also belong in this group, and the chemistry of diphosphorus compounds generally has been reviewed by Huheey (56).

The diphosphorus halides show a curious irregularity in stability, since only the chloride and iodide, P_2Cl_4 and P_2I_4, have been prepared. Attempts to prepare the fluoride P_2F_4 (57) and the bromide have so far failed.

2. Triphosphorus (P—P—P) Compounds. There is no recorded characterization of a phosphine higher than P_2H_4, although a study of the Raman spectrum (58) of the products obtained by the decomposition of diphosphine by light and heat suggested the presence of triphosphine P_3H_5 and higher homologues in the series P_nH_{n+2}. These were not isolated, however. Van Wazer (59) has suggested that certain lower hydrides of phosphorus — amorphous yellow solids of variable composition — may consist of three-dimensional networks of singly-linked phosphorus atoms containing terminal —PH_2 groups and bridging —PH— and $>$P— units, and that it might be possible to obtain from such material molecular hydrides to continue the homologous series of which PH_3 and P_2H_4 are the only established members.

Other compounds in this group are the sulfides P_4S_3 (60) and P_4S_5 (61); $PH(CF_3)P \cdot (CF_3) \cdot PH(CF_3)$ (62) and P_3Ph_5 (63).

3. Tetraphosphorus Compounds and Higher Derivatives. Four singly-linked phosphorus atoms are present in the cyclic compounds

R = ethyl (64); n-butyl (65); cyclohexyl (66); phenyl (67); trifluoromethyl (68)

whereas a five-membered ring of phosphorus atoms is present in the compound $P_5(CF_3)_5$ (62, 68), and higher cyclic polymers $(CF_3P)_x$ can also be obtained (70). An interesting account of the phenyl polyphosphines, $(C_6H_5P)_n$, has appeared (107): it is curious that the tetramer $(C_6H_5P)_4$ ("phosphobenzene"), whose identity in benzene solution is supported by cryoscopic molecular weight measurements, is apparently derived from a *pentamer* in the solid state, according to an X-ray study.

A structure involving a six-membered ring of phosphorus atoms has been suggested (69) for the acid $H_6P_6O_{12}$, formed by the oxidation of red phosphorus with alkaline hypochlorite:

Extended systems of P—P bonds are found of course in elementary phosphorus itself — the P_4 molecule (white phosphorus) and the even more extensively polymerized red and black allotropes.

C. Arsenic, Antimony, Bismuth

The distribution of As—As bonding in arsenic compounds is curious. There are no reported hydrides or halides beyond the mononuclear AsX_3 derivatives, but there is a series of dinuclear organic derivatives of which $(CH_3)_2As$—$As(CH_3)_2$ is typical. There is then an apparent total absence of trinuclear and tetranuclear compounds, after which catenation reappears with a series of compounds containing a five-membered ring of arsenic atoms. The best-known of these compounds is "arsenomethane," $(CH_3As)_5$, which has been known since 1904; the early and rather confused literature on this substance is described by Sidgwick (71). The structure of this compound, which contains a puckered five-membered ring of As atoms with the As—As distance (2.42–2.44 Å) very close to that expected for normal two-electron covalent bonds, has been established by Burns and Waser (72):

R = CH₃

The compound forms yellow crystals, m.p. 7°C.; there is apparently a red or brown modification with m. p. 180°C. (73). A similar derivative with $R = CH_3CH_2CH_2$ has been prepared (74), but the only support for its formulation as a pentamer was a molecular weight determination.

A compound with empirical formula C_6H_5As, called "arsenobenzene," has been regarded (71) as an analogue of the azo-compounds and hence as

$$C_6H_5As = AsC_6H_5$$

with a double bond between two arsenic atoms; the drug Salvarsan is a derivative of this compound. These compounds have been studied extensively by Russian workers, who claim (75) that arsenobenzene is the cyclic hexamer

$$R = C_6H_5$$

and that there is no evidence for an $As = As$ double bond in any of the related compounds. Certainly the occurrence of double bonds formed by $p_\pi - p_\pi$ overlap is rare between atoms other than those in the first periodic row. Aqueous solutions of Salvarsan are reported (76) to contain polymerized species such as

and similar catenated products are obtained (77) by treatment of arsenomethane with iodine in benzene solution, yielding polymers like

with molecular weights of several thousands.

Catenation in arsenic compounds would appear to merit a systematic study.

In antimony and bismuth, X—X bonding is severely limited; there are (71) a small number of dinuclear compounds of antimony like

$(CH_3)_2Sb-\!-Sb(CH_3)_2$. Attempts (78) to prepare the compound C_6H_5Sb $=SbC_6H_5$ always produced polymeric products containing some oxygen; apparently Sb—Sb bonds are present but the structures of the polymers are unknown.

Catenation has virtually disappeared in bismuth. There is a report (79) of $(CH_3)_2Bi-Bi(CH_3)_2$, but the compound was highly unstable and obtained in insufficient quantity for analysis.

The diminishing tendency towards catenation observed along the series As, Sb, Bi appears to follow that in the preceding subgroup, Ge, Sn, Pb.

D. Strengths of the X—X Bonds (X = N, P, As, Sb, Bi)

The energies (24) of these bonds are as follows:

$$\bar{D}_{X-X} \text{ kcal./mole}$$

N—N	38.4
P—P	51.3
As—As	32.1
Sb—Sb	30.2
Bi—Bi	25

It is apparent that this order of energies, which follows quite closely the trend in catenation observed in the series, is the same as that for the group 4 sequence C, Si, Ge, Sn, and Pb with the striking exception of nitrogen, for which the N—N bond has a distinctly lower energy than the P—P bond. Nor is this feature confined to group 5, because in the subsequent groups the first-row members oxygen and fluorine show the same low bond energies compared with the second-row elements:

C—C	N—N	O—O	F—F
83.1	38.4	33.2	36.6

Si—Si	P—P	S—S	Cl—Cl
42.2	51.3	50.9	58.0

These "anomalously" low energies for the smallest atoms of the first row have been commonly attributed (80) to "lone-pair repulsion," i.e., to repulsion between the nonbonding electron pairs present in the valence-shells of the N, O, and F atoms in such single-bonded molecules as H_2N—NH_2, HO—OH, and F—F. This view is not shared by Mulliken, who attributed (81) the irregularities in the group 5, 6, and 7 sequences to a *strengthening* of the X—X sigma bonds in the cases of second-row elements by the participation of d orbitals in the hybrids contributing to bond formation. A recent analysis of the factors contributing to the bond energies of the diatomic halogen molecules has been made by Caldow and Coulson (82).

Although there may be some disagreement as to the cause of the low N—N bond energy, there is little doubt that the paucity of stable compounds containing such bonds is due to this factor, particularly when it is remembered that the triple bond in elementary nitrogen is exceptionally strong: $D_{N\equiv N} = 226$ kcal./mole, which is considerably more than three times the single-bond energy.

IV. CATENATION IN O, S, Se, AND Te

No compound is known in which more than two oxygen atoms are joined together by a single covalent bond; the O—O linkage is confined to hydrogen peroxide and its derivatives. In ozone O_3, and the ozonide ion O_3^-, the bonding is of course multiple, while the curious molecule O_4(24) appears to consist of two O_2 molecules held together by bonds that are much weaker than ordinary covalent bonds.

In sharp contrast are the prolific examples of —S—S— chains in sulfur compounds: There are no oxygen analogues of the familiar S_8 molecule (rhombic sulfur), or of the polysulfide ions S_n^{2-} ($n > 2$), or of the polythionate ions $(O_3S \cdot S_n \cdot SO_3)^{2-}$ ($n > 2$). Still longer chains of sulfur atoms are believed to be present in liquid sulfur, where the average chain length is about 1.5×10^6 Å at 171°C. (83) and in some polythionates, where the chain may contain up to eighty sulfur atoms (84). The extent and diversity of catenation in sulfur compounds is well illustrated in reviews by Schmidt (85) and by Feher (90). It is interesting that attempts to produce and identify *branched* sulfur chains have so far failed.

A. Selenium and Tellurium

There are very few selenium compounds containing Se—Se bonds corresponding to those formed by sulfur. The strongest resemblances are found in the element itself, thus, two allotropic modifications of selenium contain Se_8 molecules (91, 92). Grey selenium consists of infinite helical —Se—Se—Se— chains (93). Among selenium compounds there are the halides Se_2Cl_2 and Se_2Br_2, an unstable H_2Se_2 which is formed only in traces (94), and polyselenides up to M_2Se_5 (95). Organic derivatives include the diselenides $R \cdot Se_2 \cdot R$, R = alkyl or aryl (96, 97), or CF_3 (98), and the triselenides $R \cdot Se_3 \cdot R$, R = alkyl or aryl (99), or CF_3 (98).

Catenation in tellurium compounds is very rare, although the element itself is isomorphous with the chain-form of selenium (the grey allotrope). There are no halides Te_2X_2, but Te_2F_{10}, the analogue of S_2F_{10}, is known (100, 101), and it is curious that there has been no report of the corresponding selenium compound Se_2F_{10}.

Catenation in this series O, S, Se, Te therefore shows the same irregularity in trend as was observed in the previous section for N, P, As, and Sb. The paucity and high reactivity of compounds containing —O—O— bonds can again be attributed to the low O—O single-bond energy, combined with the fact that the multiple bond in molecular oxygen is well over twice as strong: $D_{O=O} = 119$ kcal./mole; there must therefore be an inherent energetic tendency for the —O—O— bond to be unstable with respect to molecular oxygen. The decrease in catenation in passing from S to Te parallels the diminishing strengths of the X—X bonds:

$$\bar{D}_{X-X}, \text{ kcal./mole}$$

	$\bar{D}_{X-X}$, kcal./mole
O—O	33.2
S—S	50.9
Se—Se	44.0
Te—Te	33

REFERENCES

(1) Borer, K., and C. S. G. Phillips, *Proc. Chem. Soc.*, **1959**, 189.

(2) MacDiarmid, A. G., in H. J. Emeleus and A. G. Sharpe, eds., *Advances in Inorganic Chemistry and Radiochemistry*, Vol. 3, Academic Press Inc., New York, 1961, p. 207.

(3) Stone, F. G. A., *Hydrogen Compounds of the Group IV Elements*, Prentice-Hall, Inc., Englewood Cliffs, New Jersey, 1962.

(4) Kaczmarczyk, A., M. Millard, and G. Urry, *J. Inorg. Nucl. Chem.*, **17**, 188 (1961); A. Kaczmarczyk, M. Millard, J. W. Nuss, and G. Urry, *J. Inorg. Nucl. Chem.*, **26**, 421 (1964).

(5) Kaczmarczyk, A., and G. Urry, *J. Am. Chem. Soc.*, **82**, 751 (1960); Kaczmarczyk, A., J. W. Nuss, and G. Urry, *J. Inorg. Nucl. Chem.*, **26**, 427 (1964).

(6) Schwarz, R., and C. Danders, *Ber.*, **80**, 441 (1947); *Z. Anorg. Allgem. Chem.*, **253**, 273 (1947).

(7) Schwarz, R., and A. Koester, *Z. Anorg. Allgem. Chem.*, **270**, 2 (1952).

(8) Emeleus, H. J., and K. Stewart, *Trans. Faraday, Soc.*, **32**, 1577 (1936).

(9) Emeleus, H. J., and C. J. Reid, *J. Chem. Soc.*, **1939**, 1021.

(10) Stock, A., P. Stiebeler, and F. Zeidler, Ber., **56B**, 1695 (1923).

(11) Schwarz, R., and F. Heinrich, *Z. Anorg. Allgem. Chem.*, **221**, 277 (1935).

(12) Schott, G., W. Herrmann, and E. Hirschmann, *Angew. Chem.*, **68**, 213 (1956).

(13) Schmeisser, M., and M. Schwarzmann, *Z. Naturforsch.*, **11b**, 278 (1956).

(14) Schmeisser, M., "Silicium, Schwefel, Phosphate", *Collog, Sek. Anorg. Chem. Intern. Union Reine u. Angew. Chem.*, Münster, 1954, p. 28–31, pub. 1955.

(15) Bonitz, E., *Ber.*, **94**, 220 (1961).

(16) Pflugmacher, A., and I. Rohrman, *Z. Anorg. Allgem. Chem.* **290**, 101 (1957).

(17) Schwarz, R., and A. Pflugmacher, *Ber.*, **75**, 1062 (1942).

(18) Burkhard, C. A., *J. Am. Chem. Soc.*, **71**, 963 (1949).

(19) Kautsky, H., and G. Herzberg, *Ber.*, **57B**, 1665 (1924); H. Kautsky, *Z. Electrochem.*, **32**, 349 (1926); H. Kautsky and A. Hirsch, *Ber.*, **64B**, 1610 (1931).

(20) Huckel, W., *Structural Chemistry of Inorganic Compounds*, Vol. II, Elsevier, New York, 1951, p. 943.

(21) Wiberg, E., and W. Simmler, *Z. Anorg. Allgem. Chem.*, **283**, 401 (1956).

(22) Wittenberg, D., M. V. George, and H. Gilman, *J. Am. Chem. Soc.*, **81**, 4812 (1959).

(23) Steele, W. C., and F. G. A. Stone, *J. Am. Chem. Soc.*, **84**, 3599 (1962).

(24) Pauling, L., *The Nature of the Chemical Bond*, 3rd ed., Cornell University Press, New York, 1960.

(25) Cottrell, T. L., *The Strengths of Chemical Bonds*, Butterworths, London, 1954.

(26) Gunn, S. R., and L. G. Green, *J. Phys. Chem.*, **65**, 779 (1961).

(27) Drake, J. E., and W. L. Jolly, *J. Chem. Soc.*, **1962**, 2807.

(28) Kraus, C. A., and E. S. Carney, *J. Am. Chem. Soc.*, **56**, 765 (1934).

(29) Dennis, L. M., and R. W. Work, *J. Am. Chem. Soc.*, **55**, 4486 (1933).

(30) Dennis, L. M., and M. A. Skow, *J. Am. Chem. Soc.*, **52**, 2369 (1930).

(31) Glarum, S. N., and C. A. Kraus, *J. Am. Chem. Soc.*, **72**, 5398 (1950).

(32) Macklen, E. D., *J. Chem. Soc.*, **1959**, 1984.

(33) Royen, P., and R. Schwarz, *Z. Anorg. Allgem. Chem.*, **211**, 412 (1933); **215**, 288, 295 (1933).

(34) Moulton, C. W., and J. G. Miller, *J. Am. Chem. Soc.*, **78**, 2702 (1956).

(35) Schwarz, R., and E. Baronetzky, *Z. Anorg. Allgem. Chem.*, **275**, 1 (1954).

(36) Bartlett, N., and K. C. Yu, *Can. J. Chem.*, **39**, 80 (1961).

(37) Powell, H. M., and F. M. Brewer, *J. Chem. Soc.*, **1938**, 197.

(38) Kraus, C. A., and C. L. Brown, *J. Am. Chem. Soc.*, **52**, 4031 (1930).

(39) Schwarz, R., and M. Schmeisser, *Ber.*, **69**, 579 (1936).

(40) Metlesics, W., and H. Zeiss, *J. Am. Chem. Soc.*, **82**, 3321 (1960).

(41) Glockling, F., and K. A. Hooton, *J. Chem. Soc.*, **1963**, 1849.

(42) Jolly, W. A., *Angew. Chem.*, **72**, 268 (1960); *J. Am. Chem. Soc.*, **83**, 335 (1961).

(43) Kraus, C. A., and W. N. Greer, *J. Am. Chem. Soc.*, **47**, 2568 (1925).

(44) Kraus, C. A., and A. M. Neal, *J. Am. Chem. Soc.*, **51**, 2405 (1929).

(45) Ingham, R. K., S. D. Rosenberg, and H. Gilman, *Chem. Rev.*, **60**, 459 (1960).

(46) Neumann, W. P., and K. Koenig, *Angew. Chem.*, **1**, 212 (1962).

(47) Jensen, K. A., and N. Clauson-Kass, *Z. Anorg. Allgem. Chem.*, **250**, 277 (1943).

(48) Calingaert, G., and H. Soros, *J. Org. Chem.*, **2**, 535 (1938).

(49) Rice, F. O., and F. Scherber, *J. Am. Chem. Soc.*, **77**, 291 (1955).

(50) Sidgwick, N. V., *The Organic Chemistry of Nitrogen*, revised edition, Oxford University Press, Oxford, 1942.

(51) Wohl, A., and H. Schiff, *Ber.*, **33**, 2741 (1900).

(52) Burg, A. B., *J. Am. Chem. Soc.*, **83**, 2226 (1961).

(53) Dörken, C., *Ber.* **21**, 1505 (1888).

(54) Maier, L., *Angew. Chem.*, **71**, 575 (1959); *Ber.*, **94**, 3043 (1961).

(55) Bennett, F. W., H. J. Emeleus, and R. N. Haszeldine, *J. Chem. Soc.*, **1953**, 1565.

(56) Huheey, J. E., *J. Chem. Educ.*, **40**, 153 (1963).

(57) Finch, A., *Can. J. Chem.*, **37**, 1793 (1959).

(58) Baudler, M., and L. Schmidt, *Naturwissenschaften*, **46**, 578 (1959).

(59) Van Wazer, J. R., *Phosphorus and its Compounds*, Interscience, New York, 1958, p. 215–219.

(60) Houten, S., A. Vox, and G. A. Wregers, *Rec. Trav. Chim.*, **74**, 1167 (1955).

(61) Houten, S., and E. H. Wiebenga, *Acta Cryst.*, **10**, 156 (1957).

(62) Mahler, W., and A. B. Burg, *J. Am. Chem. Soc.*, **80**, 6161 (1958).

(63) Kuchen, W., and H. Buchwald, *Ber.*, **91**, 2871 (1958).

(64) Isslieb, K., and B. Mitcherling, *Z. Naturforsch.*, **156**, 267 (1960).

(65) Grayson, M., *Chem. Eng. News*, Dec. 3, p. 98 (1962); Nov. 19, p. 44 (1962)

(66) Isslieb, K., and W. Seidel, *Z. Anorg. Allgem. Chem.*, **303**, 155 (1960).

(67) Kuchen, W., and H. Buchwald, *Angew. Chem.*, **68**, 791 (1956).

(68) Mahler, W., and A. B. Burg, *J. Am. Chem. Soc.*, **79**, 251 (1957).

(69) Blaser, B., and K-H. Worms, *Z. Anorg. Allgem. Chem.*, **300**, 237 (1959).

(70) Banks, R. E., and R. N. Haszeldine, in H. J. Emeleus and A. G. Sharpe, eds., *Advances in Inorganic Chemistry and Radiochemistry*, Vol. 3, Academic Press, Inc., New York, 1961, p. 337.

(71) Sidgwick, N. V., *The Chemical Elements and their Compounds*, Oxford University Press, Oxford, 1950.

(72) Burns, J. H., and J. Waser, *J. Am. Chem. Soc.*, **79**, 859 (1957).

(73) Dehn, W., *Am. Chem. J.*, **33**, 120 (1905); **40**, 108 (1908).

(74) Steinkopf, W., and H. Dudek, *Ber.*, **61**, 1906 (1928).

(75) Kraft, M. Ya, G. M. Borodina, I. N. Strel'tsova, and Yu T. Struchkov, *Dokl. Akad. Nauk SSSR.*, **131**, 1074 (1960), through *Chem. Abstr.*, **54**, 20936 (1960).

(76) Kraft, M. Ya, and I. A. Bushchuk, *Dokl. Akad. Nauk SSSR*, **65**, 509 (1949), through *Chem. Abstr.* **44**, 128 (1950).

(77) Kraft, M. Ya, and V. V. Katyshkina, *Dokl. Akad. Nauk SSSR.*, **66**, 207 (1949), through *Chem. Abstr.* **44**, 127, (1950).

(78) Klages, F., and W. Rapp, *Chem. Ber.*, **88**, 384 (1955).

(79) Paneth, F., and H. Loliet, *J. Chem. Soc.*, **1935**, 366.

(80) Pitzer, K. S., *J. Am. Chem. Soc.*, **70**, 2140 (1948).

(81) Mulliken, R. S., *J. Am. Chem. Soc.*, **72**, 4496 (1950).

(82) Caldow, G. L., and C. A. Coulson, *Trans. Faraday Soc.*, **58**, 633 (1962).

(83) Gardner, D. M., and G. K. Fraenkel, *J. Am. Chem. Soc.*, **78**, 3279 (1956).

(84) Weitz, E., *Ber.*, **89**, 2353, 2365 (1956); *Angew. Chem.*, **64**, 166 (1952).

(85) Schmidt, M., in F. G. A. Stone, ed., *Inorganic Polymers*, Academic Press, Inc., New York, 1962.

(86) Ingham, R. K., and H. Gilman, in F. G. A. Stone, ed., *Inorganic Polymers*, Academic Press, Inc., New York, 1962.

(87) Kipping, F. S., and J. E. Sands, *J. Chem. Soc.*, **119**, 848 (1921).

(88) Jarvie, A. W. P., H. J. S. Winkler, and H. Gilman, *J. Org. Chem.*, **27**, 614 (1962).

(89) Winkler, H. J. S., A. W. P. Jarvie, D. J. Peterson, and H. Gilman, *J. Am. Chem. Soc.*, **83**, 4089 (1961).

(90) Feher, F., "Long Chain Sulfur Compounds," in *Chem. Soc. London Special Publication No. 12*, 1958, p. 305.

(91) Burbank, R. D., *Acta Cryst.*, **4**, 140 (1951); **5**, 236 (1952)

(92) Marsh, R. E., L. Pauling, and J. D. McCullough, *Acta Cryst.*, **6**, 71 (1953)

(93) Cotton, C. A., and G. Wilkinson, *Advanced Inorganic Chemistry*, Interscience, New York, 1962.

(94) Nielsen, J. P., S. Maeser, and D. S. Jennings, *J. Am. Chem. Soc.*, **61**, 440 (1939).

(95) Bergstrom, F. W., *J. Am. Chem. Soc.*, **48**, 146, 2319 (1926).

(96) Backer, H. J., and W. Van Dam, *Rec. Trav. Chim.*, **54**, 531 (1935).

(97) Stoner, G. G., and R. W. Williams, *J. Am. Chem. Soc.*, **70**, 1113 (1948).

(98) Dale, J. W., H. J. Emeleus, and R. N. Haszeldine, *J. Chem. Soc.*, **1958**, 2939.

(99) Levi, G. R., and A. Baroni, *Atti Accad. Naz. Lincei.*, **9**, 1019 (1929) through *Chem. Abstr.*, **24**, 306 (1930).

(100) English, W. D., and J. W. Dale, *J. Chem. Soc.*, **1953**, 2498.

(101) Campbell, R., and P. L. Robinson, *J. Chem. Soc.*, **1956**, 3454.

(102) Hague, D. N., and R. H. Prince, *Chem. & Ind. (London)* 1492 (1964).

(103) Urry, G., *J. Inorg. Nucl. Chem.*, **26**, 409 (1964).

(104) Timms, P. L., C. C. Simpson, and C. S. G. Phillips, *J. Chem. Soc.*, **1964**, 1467.

(105) Olson, D. H., and R. E. Rundle, *Inorg. Chem.*, **2**, 1310 (1963).

(106) Neumann, W. P., *Angew. Chem.*, **75**, 225 (1963).

(107) Daly, J. J., and L. Maier, *Nature*, **203**, 1167 (1964).

(108) Gilman, H., and F. K. Cartledge, *Chem. & Ind. (London)*, 1231 (1964).

Chapter 4

Compounds Whose Instability is a Consequence of the Reluctance of Atoms of the Second (and Subsequent) Rows to Form Multiple Bonds Involving $p_\pi-p_\pi$ Overlap

I. GENERAL

One of the most striking differences in bond-forming tendencies between the first row elements (notably carbon, nitrogen, and oxygen) and their congeners in the second and subsequent rows, is the widespread occurrence in the first case, and almost total absence in the second, of compounds stable under ordinary conditions of temperature and pressure containing bonds of the type formally described in terms of $p_\pi - p_\pi$ overlap. In this chapter silicon is first compared with carbon in this respect. Similar comparisons between phosphorus and nitrogen, and sulfur and oxygen, are then made and the theoretical aspects are considered.

II. SILICON

A. Comparison with Carbon Compounds

True iso-structural analogues (formulas shown below), stable under ordinary conditions, of multiple-bonded carbon compounds such as olefins, acetylenes, aldehydes, ketones, nitriles, carbon dioxide, carbon disulfide, and the carbonate ion, have not been prepared, nor has an allotropic modification of elementary silicon corresponding to graphite:

61

$$\begin{array}{c} R \\ \diagdown \\ R \diagup \end{array} Si = Si \begin{array}{c} R \\ \diagup \\ \diagdown R \end{array} \qquad R-Si\equiv Si-R \qquad \begin{array}{c} R \\ \diagdown \\ H \diagup \end{array} Si = O \qquad \begin{array}{c} R \\ \diagdown \\ R \diagup \end{array} Si = O$$

$$R-Si\equiv N \qquad O = Si = O \qquad S = Si = S \qquad \begin{array}{c} {}^{-}O \\ \diagdown \\ {}_{-}O \diagup \end{array} Si = O$$

If these structures were adopted, then in each case it would be possible to construct the Si—to—X multiple bond from a σ-component together with a π-component (or two π-components in the case of a triple bond) resulting from the "sideways" overlap of silicon $3p_\pi$ orbitals with the p_π orbitals of the second atom X. For example, the silico-ethylene molecule $H_2Si = SiH_2$ can be built up (in valence-bond terms) from two Si atoms each with electron configuration $1s^2\, 2s^2\, 2p^6\, 3s^2\, 3p^2$, in which the valence-shell orbitals are then hybridized to give a set of three trigonal sp^2 hybrid orbitals and a remaining $3p_z$ orbital normal to the trigonal plane:

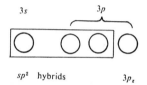

$3s$ $3p$

sp^2 hybrids $3p_z$

The planar

$$\begin{array}{c} H \\ \diagdown \\ H \diagup \end{array} Si - Si \begin{array}{c} H \\ \diagup \\ \diagdown H \end{array}$$

sigma-bonded skeleton is then formed by use of the three sp^2 hybrid orbitals on each silicon; the remaining $3p_z$ orbitals may then overlap above and below the plane of the other atoms to form a second bond, of the π-type, between the two silicon atoms.

In fact, the formation of such multiple bonds seems always to be avoided. Compounds with the same *empirical* formulas as the carbon analogues are known and discussed below, but their structures are always polymerized in such a way that each $p_\pi - p_\pi$ bond is replaced by a bond of the sigma type. It must be made clear at this stage that it is only a particular type of π-bond — that resulting from the overlap of two p_π orbitals — which is so rarely formed by silicon and other second row elements. Multiple bonds in which the $3d$ *orbitals* of the second row elements contribute to the π-component are well-known and are of widespread occurrence. For example, Cruickshank (1) has reviewed the available bond-length data for Si—O bonds and has pointed out that all the known Si—O distances are within 0.03 Å of 1.63 Å — even those conventionally formulated as single bonds, as in tetramethyl silicate,

$$\begin{array}{c}
CH_3O \\ \diagdown \\ \end{array} Si \begin{array}{c} \diagup OCH_3 \\ \\ \end{array}$$
$$\begin{array}{c} CH_3O \diagup \end{array} \begin{array}{c} \diagdown OCH_3 \end{array}$$

This distance is significantly shorter than the sum of the covalent radii (2):

$$r_{Si} + r_O = 1.17 + 0.74 = 1.91 \text{ Å}$$

Application of the empirical (3) and much-criticized (4) Schomaker-Stevenson correction for partial ionic character reduces this value to 1.76 Å, but even this is distinctly longer than the experimental distances. It seems to be widely agreed that the short Si—O distances are a consequence of partial multiple-bond character in the Si—O bond, resulting from the "back coordination" of the lone-pair p_π electrons on the oxygen atoms into the vacant $3d$ orbitals on silicon. Formation of this type of $3d_\pi - p_\pi$ bond is well-known for atoms beyond those of the first row.

B. Iso-Structural Analogues

Silicon compounds which may conceivably contain $p_\pi - p_\pi$ bonds comprise a very small group.

1. Silicon Monoxide, SiO. This molecule, the analogue of carbon monoxide, CO, undoubtedly exists as a monomeric $p_\pi - p_\pi$ bonded species in the gas phase at high temperatures; it has been indentified spectroscopically (5) and by means of the mass spectrometer (6). A survey of its thermodynamic properties has been made by Brewer and Edwards (7) who conclude that silicon monoxide is formed quantitatively in the gas phase from silicon dioxide and elemental silicon at high temperatures. There is a voluminous and rather contradictory literature on the solid phase formed by quenching the vapor. A number of claims have been made that the colored solid of empirical composition SiO is a distinct chemical species on the basis of X-ray diffraction experiments; in particular it seems that a diffraction ring corresponding to a d-spacing of 3.60 Å is characteristic of the material (7, 8, 9, 10, 11). Other reports (12, 13) claim from similar experiments that the solid is merely an equimolar mixture of silicon and silicon dioxide. Whatever the truth of the matter, it is clear that if silicon monoxide does exist under ordinary conditions (as distinct from conditions of high temperature, where there is no dispute), then it exists in the form of a solid which is undoubtedly polymerized and is quite different in structure from the corresponding monomeric carbon compound CO.

2. Silicoformaldehyde ("Protosiloxane"), H_2SiO. Stock and his coworkers, in the course of the investigation of the hydrolysis of dichloromonosilane SiH_2Cl_2, reported (14, 15) the formation of a gaseous product which they considered to be the monomer

$$\begin{matrix} H \\ \diagdown \\ \diagup \\ H \end{matrix} Si=O$$

the analogue of formaldehyde. The gaseous compound however was extraordinarily susceptible to polymerization and rapidly condensed to liquid and solid products of the same composition, $(H_2SiO)_n$. The liquid, which was soluble in benzene, gave a molecular weight corresponding roughly with its formulation as a hexamer, $(H_2SiO)_6$. The solid polymer, a white amorphous substance resembling silicic acid in appearance, was insoluble and nonvolatile; there is no information concerning its structure but undoubtedly it is polymerized through Si—O—Si linkages.

3. Silicon-to-Carbon Multiple Bonds. A compound, announced (16) as the first of its type and considered to have structure (**1**), involving a $Si=C$ double bond, was subsequently shown (17) to be the single-bonded isomer (**2**):

$$\begin{matrix} CH_3 & & CH_3 \\ \diagdown & & \diagup \\ & Si=CH \cdot Si-CH_3 \\ \diagup & & \diagdown \\ CH_3 & & CH_3 \end{matrix} \qquad \begin{matrix} CH_3 & CH_2 & CH_3 \\ \diagdown & \diagup & \diagup \\ Si & & Si \\ \diagup & \diagdown & \diagdown \\ CH_3 & CH_2 & CH_3 \end{matrix}$$

$$(\mathbf{1}) \qquad\qquad\qquad (\mathbf{2})$$

C. Polymerized Analogues

In virtually all other cases, there is no doubt that silicon analogues of multiple-bonded carbon compounds have polymerized structures. Some examples are discussed below.

1. Silico-Ethylenes and Acetylenes. Silicon compounds corresponding to the monomeric species ethylene and acetylene may be produced as short-lived reaction intermediates, but polymerize too rapidly to be isolated; inevitably reactions which might be expected to yield $H_2Si=SiH_2$

or $HSi \equiv SiH$ produce solid polymers. For example, Schwarz and Hein-rich (18) obtained a compound of composition $(SiH_2)_n$, "polysilene," as a light-brown solid which exploded spontaneously in air, and $(SiH)_n$ has been prepared (19) as a hard, brittle polymeric yellow solid. In these compounds the multiple bonds of the carbon monomers have obviously been replaced by an equivalent number of single bonds:

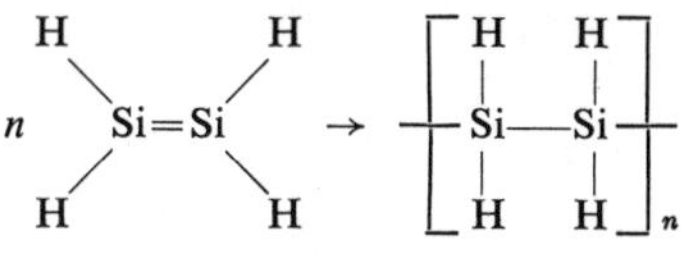

2. Analogues of CO_2, CS_2, and Carbonates. The well-known differ-ences in melting point between carbon dioxide and carbon disulfide and the corresponding silicon compounds reflect profound differences in structure:

	m. p., °C.
CO_2	−78.5 (subl.)
CS_2	−112.1
SiO_2 (cristobalite)	1728
SiS_2	high (subl.)

Whereas the carbon compounds form multiple-bonded monomers to whose structures the forms $O=C=O$ and $S=C=S$ make the greatest contributions, silicon dioxide SiO_2 in its various forms has a giant lattice extending infinitely in three dimensions, and silicon disulfide SiS_2 adopts a nonmolecular chain structure (20):

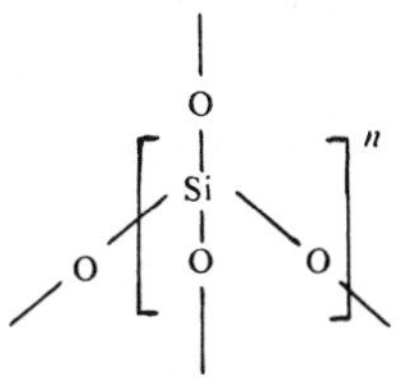

$(SiO_2)_n$ 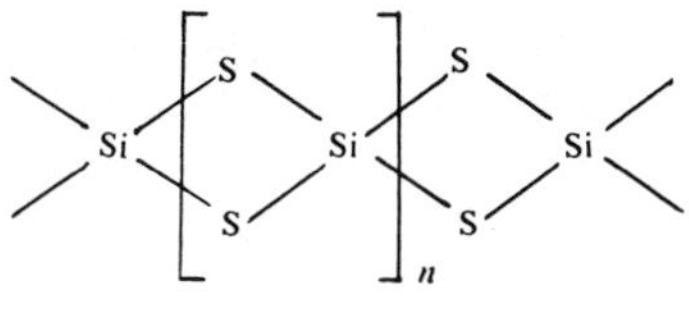 $(SiS_2)_n$

Again the basic skeleton is single-bonded, any multiple-bond character resulting from the donation of oxygen or sulfur atom lone-pairs into the vacant silicon $3d$ orbitals.

Similarly, the three-coordinate carbonate ion $CO_3{}^{2-}$ exists as a discrete anion in many ionic carbonates. These have as their analogues in silicon chemistry the great diversity of polymerized silicate structures in which the silicon atom is invariably linked to a tetrahedron of oxygen atoms; the metasilicate chains of the pyroxene minerals are typical (20):

$$(SiO_3{}^{2-})_n$$

3. Silico-Ketones. The term "silicone" was given by F. S. Kipping to the products formed by elimination of water from silanediols of formula $R_2Si(OH)_2$, because of their resemblance in formula (R_2SiO) to the organic ketones (R_2CO), although he recognized that their structures must be of a fundamentally different type. The name "silicone" has of course persisted today as a convenient generic term for the large number of important polymers of which Kipping's compounds were prototypes (21).

There is no record of the preparation of a stable monomer

and reactions expected to lead to their formation always produce polymers. For example, Hyde and De Long (22) showed that the silicon analogue of diethyl ketone is a cyclic polymer: treatment of $(C_2H_5)_2SiCl_2$ with water yielded a heterogeneous liquid product of which the major component was the trimer $(C_4H_{10}SiO)_3$, presumably with the cyclic structure

$$Et = C_2H_5$$

Similar cyclic trimers were obtained by the hydrolysis of $(C_6H_5)_2$ $SiCl_2$ and $(C_6H_5)(C_2H_5)SiCl_2$.

4. Silico-Oxalic Acid. Silicon analogues (RSiOOH) of the carboxylic acids RCOOH have quite different properties, again in accordance with their possessing polymerized structures. For example, "silico-oxalic acid," $(SiOOH)_2$, has been prepared and even forms a "dihydrate" like the carbon compound, but it is an insoluble nonacidic polymeric solid which decomposes on treatment with bases, evolving hydrogen gas; no salt is formed (23).

III. PHOSPHORUS

Nitrogen compounds formulated with $p_\pi - p_\pi$ bonds are abundant and include (in addition to elemental nitrogen, N_2) the oxides N_2O, NO, N_2O_3, NO_2, N_2O_4, and N_2O_5; hydrazoic acid HN_3 and the azides; the oxyacids hyponitrous acid $H_2N_2O_2$, nitrous acid HNO_2, nitric acid HNO_3 and the corresponding oxyanions $N_2O_2^{2-}$, NO_2^-, and NO_3^-; and the nitrosonium and nitronium ions NO^+ and NO_2^+. No true iso-structural analogues of any of these species, stable under ordinary conditions, are known among phosphorus compounds.

The absence of $p_\pi - p_\pi$ bonding in phosphorus chemistry is typified by the element itself. There is only one molecular form of elemental nitrogen — the very stable N_2 molecule. Its phosphorus analogue does indeed exist, but only in the gas phase at temperatures over 800°C.

Not only is the $P \equiv P$ triple bond much weaker than the $N \equiv N$ triple bond,

$$P_2(g) \rightarrow 2\,P(g) \qquad \Delta H^0 = +116.8 \text{ kcal./mole } P_2 \quad (24)$$

cf.

$$N_2(g) \rightarrow 2\,N(g) \qquad \Delta H^0 = +226.0 \text{ kcal./mole } N_2 \quad \text{(Table 1.3)}$$

but the P_2 molecule is unstable with respect to the tetrahedral molecule P_4, white phosphorus:

$$2\,P_2(g) \rightarrow P_4(s, \alpha \text{ modification}) \qquad \Delta H^0 = -68.5 \text{ kcal./mole } P_4 \quad (24)$$

in which each phosphorus atom forms three single sigma bonds to three other P atoms. White phosphorus is not the most stable form of elemental phosphorus; the other solid forms (red and black phosphorus) are extensively polymerized networks of singly-linked phosphorus atoms (20).

Gas-phase species such as PN, PC, and PO have been identified spectroscopically (25) and undoubtedly contain multiple bonds, but the simple diatomic molecules do not survive condensation. Many phosphorus nitrides are known, some of which approach the composition PN (25), but they are solid, obviously polymerized substances. Similarly, $(PO)_n$ (cf. NO) is a brown polymeric solid formed (26) by the reaction of $POBr_3$ with magnesium in ether; $(PS)_n$ is a yellow, insoluble polymerized sulfide obtained in a similar fashion (27) from $PSBr_3$.

The oxide of composition PO_2 (cf. NO_2) is polymerized even in the vapor phase, where its molecular weight ranges from 293 to 721 (28), while P_4O_6 and P_4O_{10} (cf. N_2O_3 and N_2O_5) have the well-known structures related to the P_4 tetrahedron.

IV. SULFUR

The sulfur analogue $S_2(g)$ of the multiple-bonded oxygen molecule O_2 exists in sulfur vapor at high temperatures and has been identified spectroscopically. Furthermore it can be obtained as a purple paramagnetic solid by shock-cooling the vapor to $-196°C$. (29, 30, 31). The solid S_2 however rapidly reverts to rhombic sulfur even at $-80°C$. and is thus highly unstable. The strength of the multiple bond in S_2 can be assessed from its heat of dissociation (32, 33):

$$S_2(g) \rightarrow 2\,S(g) \qquad \Delta H^0 = 102 \text{ kcal./mole } S_2$$

The bond is thus rather weaker than that in O_2:

$$O_2(g) \rightarrow 2\,O(g) \qquad \Delta H^0 = 119.1 \text{ kcal./mole } O_2 \quad \text{(Table 1.3)}$$

However, the heat of formation of $S_2(g)$ (34) indicates that it is unstable with respect to the single-bonded S_8 allotrope (rhombic sulfur) which is the stable form of the element under ordinary conditions:

$$4\,S_2(g) \rightarrow S_8(s, \text{ rhombic}) \qquad \Delta H^0 = -123.4 \text{ kcal./mole } S_8$$

The widespread occurrence of S—S single bonds (discussed in Chapter 3, Section IV) confirms the preference of sulfur for single-bonded rather than double $p_\pi - p_\pi$ bonded structures. Nevertheless there are a number of well-known and stable sulfur species in which $p_\pi - p_\pi$ bonding appears to be present, and the most familiar examples are compounds containing

the $>C=S$ group, for example CS_2, COS, and $CSCl_2$, which are all monomeric, unpolymerized molecules. The thioaldehydes and thioketones
however are very difficult to obtain in monomeric form and readily form
dimers and trimers, as in the case of thioformaldehyde (35):

Sulfur dioxide, when formulated as a resonance hybrid of the canonical
forms

involves a $p_\pi - p_\pi$ S—O bond; there will also be a contribution of $d_\pi - p_\pi$
bonding, resulting from overlap of the lone-pair oxygen orbitals with the
vacant sulfur $3d$ orbitals. In view of the general preference of second row
atoms single-bonded structures, it is surprising that sulfur dioxide does
not polymerize, particularly since sulfur trioxide SO_3 easily polymerizes
to form a cyclic trimer (36)

and more extensively polymerized asbestoslike forms (37), and selenium
dioxide (which consists of discrete SeO_2 molecules in the gas phase) forms
a crystalline chain-polymer solid (38):

V. ELEMENTS BEYOND THE SECOND ROW

The foregoing discussion has been confined largely to second row elements, but the paucity of compounds exhibiting $p_\pi-p_\pi$ bonding is equally marked for heavier atoms. In some cases compounds which were formerly thought to contain such a bond have been shown to be single-bonded polymers; this is the case for the phosphorus, arsenic, and antimony analogues of azobenzene, C_6H_5—X=X—C_6H_5 (X = P, As, Sb). For example, the phosphorus compound "phosphobenzene" has the cyclic structure

$$C_6H_5 \cdot P\!\!-\!\!P \cdot C_6H_5$$
$$C_6H_5 \cdot P\!\!-\!\!P \cdot C_6H_5$$

and has been discussed, together with the arsenic and antimony compounds, in Chapter 3, Sections III B and III C.

In other cases, true monomeric double-bonded species appear to exist, such as carbony selenide, COSe (O=C=Se) (39,40), thiocarbonyl selenide, CSSe (S=C=Se)(41,42), and even thiocarbonyl telluride, CSTe (S=C=Te) (43).

The group 6 analogues of the ketones,

$$\underset{R}{\overset{R}{\diagdown}}C\!\!=\!\!X \qquad (X = O, S, Se, Te)$$

show an unexpected divergence from the expected structures in the case of the tellurium compounds. As has been mentioned earlier, the sulfur compounds (X = S) are difficult to obtain in the monomeric condition because of ready polymerization; the selenium compounds (X = Se) appear to be dimeric (44), presumably

$$\underset{R}{\overset{R}{\diagdown}}C\underset{Se}{\overset{Se}{\diagup\diagdown}}C\underset{R}{\overset{R}{\diagup}}$$

but the tellurium compounds (X = Te) are all more volatile than the selenoketones, and cryoscopic measurements on benzene solutions have established (45) that they are monomeric, indicating a reversion to the double-bonded structure

$$\underset{R}{\overset{R}{\diagdown}}C\!\!=\!\!Te$$

The tervalent arsenic oxides R—As=O, which are usually volatile, low-melting solids soluble in organic solvents (46), appear from their formulas to contain a $p_\pi - p_\pi$ component in the As=O bond; the corresponding antimony compounds however, for example C_6H_5SbO, are insoluble amorphous solids which are apparently polymerized:

$$\begin{array}{ccc} O & O & O \\ Sb & Sb & Sb \\ | & | & | \\ Ph & Ph & Ph \end{array} \qquad Ph = C_6H_5$$

VI. THEORETICAL CONSIDERATIONS

The preference of second row atoms for single-bonded structures has been interpreted by Pitzer (47) as arising in the following way: The

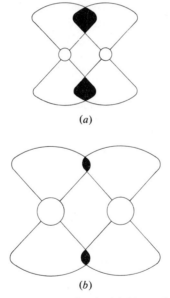

(a)

(b)

Figure 4.1. $p_\pi - p_\pi$ overlap in (a) N_2, and (b) P_2.

atoms of the second and subsequent rows all have inner electron shells which are larger (with respect to both size and content of electrons) than those of the first row; consequently X—X single bond interatomic distances (Table 4.1) are all larger for second-row atoms because of the increased repulsive forces between the inner shell electrons of one atom and the bonding orbital of the other. If a multiple bond is to be formed, the p_y or p_z orbitals must approach sufficiently closely to form the π-component of the multiple bond by overlapping in "sideways" fashion, and effective achievement of this is prevented by the repulsive effect of the large inner shells. This is represented diagrammatically for the nitrogen and phosphorus molecules N_2 and P_2 in Figure 4.1, which has been drawn according to Pitzer's (47) procedure. In the figure, the inner shells have been drawn proportional to Pauling's (2) univalent radii for the ions N^{5+} ($r = 0.11$ Å) and P^{5+} ($r = 0.34$ Å), and the outer radii of the p_z orbitals are 0.9 times the Pauling (2) van der Waals radii for $N(r = 1.5$ Å) and $P(r = 1.9$ Å); the corners of the p_z orbitals have been rounded somewhat. The internuclear distances are those observed experimentally for the N_2 molecule (1.094 Å) and the P_2 molecule (1.894 Å) (48). From this rough representation, the poor $p_\pi - p_\pi$ overlap in the P_2 molecule is evident, and a plausible explanation of the observed facts is thus provided. It can also be readily understood why π-bonds of the $3d_\pi - p_\pi$ type are readily formed by second row atoms, since the lobes of a $3d$ orbital are directed *towards* those of the p_π orbital, giving rise to more effective overlap.

Table 4.1

X—X Single-Bond Interatomic Distances, Å

C—C	N—N	O—O	F—F
1.54	1.47	1.47	1.42
Si—Si	P—P	S—S	Cl—Cl
2.34	2.20	2.08	1.98
Ge—Ge	As—As	Se—Se	Br—Br
2.44	2.50	2.34	2.28
Sn—Sn	Sb—Sb	Te—Te	I—I
2.80	2.86	2.76	2.67

Data from Pauling (2).

However, Mulliken (49) sought more quantitative evidence for the effect postulated by Pitzer by evaluating the overlap integral S (see Chapter 3, Section II C)

$$S = \int \psi_1 \cdot \psi_2 \cdot dv$$

for various types of bond formed between pairs of atoms from the first and second rows. The values of the overlap integrals for $p_\sigma - p_\sigma$ and $p_\pi - p_\pi$ bonds are shown in Table 4.2. The observed (or estimated) internuclear distances (R) are also shown, together with values of the quantity $R/2r$, where r is the distance from the nucleus of the maximum in the radial probability distribution curve corresponding to the Slater-type atomic orbital used.

Table 4.2

Overlap Integrals (S)

	C—C	C=C	N—N	N=N	O—O	O=O	F—F
Internuclear distance, R(Å)	1.54	1.34	1.47	1.24	1.47	1.21	1.44
$R/2r$	1.18	1.03	1.36	1.15	1.58	1.30	1.77
S, $2p_\sigma - 2p_\sigma$	0.33	0.32	0.29	0.33	0.23	0.31	0.17
S, $2p_\pi - 2p_\pi$		0.27		0.22		0.15	
Bond energy, $\bar{D}$ (kcal./mole)	83.1		38.4		33.2		36.6

	Si—Si	Si=Si	P—P	P=P	S—S	S=S	Cl—Cl
Internuclear distance, R(Å)	2.32	2.14	2.20	2.00	2.10	1.89	1.99
$R/2r$	0.91	0.84	1.02	0.93	1.12	1.00	1.19
S, $3p_\sigma - 3p_\sigma$	0.37	0.35	0.38	0.38	0.36	0.38	0.34
S, $3p_\pi - 3p_\pi$		0.33		0.27		0.22	
Bond energy, $\bar{D}$ (kcal./mole)	42.2		51.3		50.9		58.0

It can be seen from Table 4.2 that, in contrast to Pitzer's suggestion, the integrals for $p_\pi - p_\pi$ overlap are actually higher for the second row atoms than for the first. Of considerable interest are the values of $R/2r$; a figure near unity for this quantity would normally be expected. It can be seen that for single bonds formed by the first row atoms N, O, and F, the value of $R/2r$ is very much greater than unity, indicating that the internuclear distance R is abnormally long in these cases. The long bond lengths, and associated low bond energies for N—N, O—O, and F—F have been discussed in Chapter 3, Section III D, and are usually attributed to "lone pair repulsion," i.e., to repulsion between the nonbonding electron pairs in single-bonded molecules such as $H_2N—NH_2$, $HO—OH$, and $F—F$. For the second row atoms P, S, and Cl the values of $R/2r$ for single bonds are all very much smaller, the overlap integrals larger, and the corresponding bond energies higher. The changes in $R/2r$ and in S for double bonds are in the same direction, but are of smaller magnitude. Mulliken accordingly argues that the preference which second row atoms have for single-bonded structures is "not the result of *loosening* of multiple bonds for these atoms as compared with the first row atoms, but of a *lesser tightening* for multiple than for single bonds." Mulliken's argument is hardly satisfactory for carbon and silicon, for while the overlap integral for $p_\sigma - p_\sigma$ bonding is higher for Si—Si bonds than for C—C bonds, the mean energy of the Si—Si bonds in elemental silicon is barely half that of the C—C bonds in the iso-structural diamond crystal. A possible uncertainty in the value of $\bar{D}_{Si-Si}$ is discussed in Chapter 3, Section II C.

The strength of the second row atom X—X single bonds (again with the apparent exception of Si—Si) has been suggested by Mulliken to accrue at least in part from the participation of d orbitals in the $3p_\sigma - 3p_\sigma$ bonds, i.e., the bonds are formed not by pure $3p$ orbitals but by hybrids which incorporate some $3d$ character. More recent calculations of overlap integrals (50) for bonds involving d orbitals suggest that this effect could not be very large.

Finally, in assessing the significance of the overlap integrals in Table 4.2 it should be remembered that (a) the overlap integral is not an infallible index of bond strength; (b) the Slater-type orbitals used in their evaluation involve empirical constants; (c) the values of the integrals shown in the Table refer to the overlap of pure p orbitals, and take no account of hybridization; and (d) the internuclear distances for N=N and P=P bonds are only estimated values, derived from Pauling's tabulated (2) covalent double-bond radii.

The problem of the preferential adoption of single-bonded structures by second row atoms can thus hardly be regarded as completely solved. Beattie and Gilson (51) have suggested that single-bonded structures are preferred because they permit a more efficient filling of the d orbitals in second row atoms, but the significance of this effect is difficult to assess quantitatively.

REFERENCES

(1) Cruickshank, D. W. J., *J. Chem. Soc.*, **1961**, 5486.

(2) Pauling, L., *The Nature of the Chemical Bond*, 3rd ed., Cornell University Press, Ithaca, New York, 1960.

(3) Schomaker, V., and D. P. Stevenson, *J. Am. Chem. Soc.*, **63**, 37 (1941).

(4) Wells, A. F., *J. Chem. Soc.*, **1949**, 55.

(5) Rowlinson, H. C., and R. F. Barrow, *J. Chem. Phys.*, **21**, 378 (1953).

(6) Porter, R. F., W. A. Chupka, and M. G. Inghram, *J. Chem. Phys.*, **23**, 216 (1955).

(7) Brewer, L., and R. K. Edwards, *J. Phys. Chem.*, **58**, 351 (1954).

(8) Inuzuka, H., *Mazda Kenkyu Ziho*, **15**, 305 (1940), through *Chem. Abstr.*, **36**, 4001 (1942).

(9) Beletskii, M. S., and M. B. Rapoport, *Dokl. Akad. Nauk SSSR*, **72**, 699 (1950), through *Chem. Abstr.* **44**, 9844 (1950).

(10) Hoch, M., and H. L. Johnston, *J. Am. Chem. Soc.*, **75**, 5224 (1953).

(11) Klug, H. P., in M. Cannon Sneed and R. C. Brasted, eds., *Comprehensive Inorganic Chemistry*, Vol. 7, Van Nostrand, New York, 1958.

(12) Baumann, H. N. Jr., *Trans. Am. Electrochem. Soc.*, **80**, 95 (1941).

(13) Brady, G. W., *J. Chem. Phys.*, **63**, 1119 (1959).

(14) Stock, A., C. Somieski, and R. Wintgen, *Ber.*, **50**, 1764 (1917).

(15) Stock, A., and C. Somieski, *Ber.*, **52**, 1851 (1919).

(16) Fritz, G., and J. Grobe, *Z. Anorg. Allgem. Chem.*, **311**, 325 (1961).

(17) Fritz, G., W. Kemmerling, G. Sonntag, H. J. Becher, and E. A. V. Ebsworth, *Z. Anorg. Allgem. Chem.*, **321**, 10 (1963).

(18) Schwarz, R., and F. Heinrich, *Z. Anorg. Allgem. Chem.*, **221**, 273 (1935).

(19) Schott, G., W. Herrmann, and E. Hirschmann, *Angew. Chem.*, **68**, 213 (1956).

(20) Wells, A. F., *Structural Inorganic Chemistry*, 3rd ed., Clarendon Press, Oxford, 1960.

(21) Barry, A. J., and H. N. Beck, in F. G. A. Stone and W. A. G. Graham, eds., *Inorganic Polymers*, Academic Press Inc., New York, 1962.

(22) Hyde, J. F., and R. C. De Long, *J. Am. Chem. Soc.*, **63**, 1194 (1962).

(23) Friedel, C., and A. Ladenburg, *Ann. Chim. Phys.*, **19**, 390 (1880).

(24) Hartley, S. B., W. S. Holmes, J. K. Jacques, M. F. Mole, and J. C. McCoubrey, *Quart. Rev. (London)*, **17**, 204 (1963).

(25) Van Wazer, J. R., *Phosphorus and its Compounds*, Vol. I, Interscience, Inc., New York, 1958.

(26) Spandau, H., and A. Beyer, *Naturwissenschaften*, **46**, 400 (1959).

(27) Kuchen, W., and H. G. Beckers, *Angew. Chem.*, **71**, 163 (1959).

(28) Emmett, P. H., and J. F. Schulz, *Ind. Eng. Chem.*, **31**, 105 (1939).

(29) Rice, F. O., and C. Sparrow, *J. Am. Chem. Soc.*, **75**, 848 (1953).

(30) Rice, F. O., and J. Ditter, *J. Am. Chem. Soc.*, **75**, 6066 (1953).

(31) Freund, T., S. Adler and C. Sparrow, *J. Chem. Phys.*, **21**, 180 (1953).

(32) Brewer, L., *J. Chem. Phys.*, **31**, 1143 (1959).

(33) Colin, R., P. Goldfinger, and M. Jeunnehomme, *Nature*, **187**, 408 (1960).

(34) Lewis, G. N., and M. Randall, *Thermodynamics*, revised by K. S. Pitzer and L. Brewer, 2nd ed., McGraw-Hill, New York, 1961.

(35) Moerman, N. F., and E. H. Wiebenga, *Z. Krist.*, **97**, 323 (1937).

(36) Westrik, R., and C. H. McGillivray, *Rec. Trav. Chim.*, **60**, 794 (1941).

(37) Westrik, R., and C. H. McGillivray, *Acta Cryst.*, **7**, 764 (1954).

(38) McCullough, J. D., *J. Am. Chem. Soc.*, **59**, 789 (1937).

(39) Pearson, T. G., and P. L. Robinson, *J. Chem. Soc.*, **1932**, 652.

(40) Purcell, R. H., and F. D. Zahoorbox, *J. Chem. Soc.*, **1937**, 1029.

(41) Stock, A., and E. Willfroth, *Ber.*, **47**, 144 (1914).

(42) Briscoe, H. A. V., J. B. Peel, and P. L. Robinson, *J. Chem. Soc.*, **1929**, 1048.

(43) Stock, A., and P. Praetorius, *Ber.*, **47**, 131 (1914).

(44) Lyons, R. E., and W. E. Bradt, *Ber.*, **60**, 824 (1927).

(45) Lyons, R. E., and E. D. Scudder, *Ber.*, **64**, 530 (1931).

(46) Sidgwick, N. V., *The Chemical Elements and their Compounds*, Clarendon Press, Oxford, 1950.

(47) Pitzer, K. S., *J. Am. Chem. Soc.*, **70**, 2140 (1948).

(48) Cottrell, T. L., *The Strengths of Chemical Bonds*, Butterworths, London, 1954.

(49) Mulliken, R. S., *J. Am. Chem. Soc.* **72**, 4496 (1950).

(50) Craig, D. P., A. Maccoll, R. S. Nyholm, L. E. Orgel, and L. E. Sutton, *J. Chem. Soc.*, **1954**, 341.

(51) Beattie, I. R., and T. Gilson, *Nature*, **193**, 1041 (1962).

Chapter 5

Compounds Whose Instability has been Attributed to the Operation of an "Inert Pair Effect"

I. GENERAL

In the groups of elements following the transition series, particularly among the heavier members of each group, it is apparent that a tendency exists to form compounds in which two of the valence electrons are neither ionized nor occupied in covalent bond formation. The most familiar examples are the cations Tl^+, Pb^{2+}, and Bi^{3+} formed by thallium, lead, and bismuth. For these elements the highest oxidation state or "group valence" is usually unstable in the sense that its compounds are easily reduced, and in cases where the negative radical or anion is particularly susceptible to oxidation (e.g., $TlBr_3$, $PbBr_4$, PbI_4, $BiCl_5$, $BiBr_5$, BiI_5) may never have been prepared.

This state of affairs has been ascribed (1,2) to the operation of an "inert pair effect," according to which two of the valence electrons (the s^2 pair) become progressively less reactive as each group is descended.

In this chapter, the elements of groups 3, 4, and 5 are examined in turn. In each case the empirical evidence for the trend is considered, and an analysis is then made of the factors which might contribute to its operation. All compounds in which an unshared ns^2 electron pair is present in the valence shell will be discussed, although it is not uncommon to restrict the term "inert pair" to cases where the two electrons are both chemically and stereochemically inert. This more restrictive definition will not be adopted initially, as the existence of the lower valence state, whatever the geometry of the unshared pair may be, is itself of considerable interest in the cases of groups 3 (B, Al, Ga, In, Tl) and 4 (C, Si,

77

Ge, Sn, Pb). In group 5 (N, P, As, Sb, Bi) however, the mere existence of compounds containing an unshared pair of electrons is usually unremarkable, since it is then a straightforward consequence of the circumstance that group 5 elements can achieve a valence-shell octet (noble gas configuration) by the formation of three covalent bonds, for example NH_3, PCl_3, et cetera. In this group, then, we must look for compounds in which the element concerned carries an unshared electron pair for other reasons, and restrict the term "inert pair" to ions like Bi^{3+}, which does not have a noble gas configuration and so cannot be accounted for on that basis. In the subsequent groups (6 and 7) a corresponding "inert pair effect" becomes more difficult to discern and its connection with the theme of this book too tenuous to warrant discussion.

II. GROUP 3: B, Al, Ga, In, Tl

A. Boron and Aluminum

In the group 3 sequence the atoms have ns^2np^1 valence-shell configurations, with three electrons available for bond formation, and the formation of any compound in which the central atom carries an unshared valence pair of electrons shall be regarded as evidence for the inert pair effect. The formation of superficially monovalent compounds with empirical formulas BX, AlX, et cetera is not in itself evidence for the effect in the absence of structural information. For example, diboron tetrachloride B_2Cl_4 on thermal decomposition yields a number of products, some of which have the composition BCl. If these compounds were formulatable as ionic salts B^+Cl^-, then the ion B^+ would indeed contain an inert pair, but this is not the case. Two of the compounds are polymers $B_4Cl_4(3)$

and $B_8Cl_8(4)$

$$
\begin{array}{ccc}
\text{Cl} & \text{Cl} & \text{Cl} \\
\diagdown & | & \diagup \\
\text{B}-\text{B}-\text{B} & & \\
| & & | \\
\text{Cl}-\text{B} & & \text{B}-\text{Cl} \\
| & & | \\
\text{B}-\text{B}-\text{B} & & \\
\diagup & | & \diagdown \\
\text{Cl} & \text{Cl} & \text{Cl}
\end{array}
$$

in which the boron atoms are using all three of their valence electrons for covalent bond formation.

There are simple monomeric molecules like BF and AlF which have been identified spectroscopically in the gas phase, but there is no structural evidence for the existence of such species under ordinary conditions; a white solid of approximate composition AlF obtained from the vapor has been shown (5) by X-ray diffraction to be a mixture of the trifluoride AlF_3 and metallic aluminum, and the unipositive aluminum species obtained in aqueous solution by anodic oxidation is short-lived (6).

Satisfactory evidence for a cation M^+ is found for the first time in this group with gallium, Ga.

B. Gallium

Gas phase molecules GaX (X = H, OH, F, Cl, Br, I) are known (7) from spectroscopic observations; there are also many solid compounds whose compositions suggest the presence of unipositive gallium. In the absence of structural information it is difficult to say whether these compounds contain the simple species Ga^+ (the gallous ion) or whether they contain systems of Ga—Ga bonds utilizing all three valence electrons, as in the $(BCl)_n$ compounds described above. Examples of apparently monovalent gallium compounds which have been reported are Ga_2O(8), Ga_2S (9), and Ga_2Se and Ga_2Te (10). Unstable solid monohalides of rather variable composition have also been obtained; their formulas approach GaCl (11) and GaI (12).

It is the gallium "dihalides," of composition GaX_2, which provide the most conclusive evidence for the gallous ion Ga^+. Substances of composition GaX_2 can be formulated in various ways: (1) as compounds Ga^{2+} $2X^-$ or X—Ga—X, in which a single valence electron remains unpaired; (2) as Ga—Ga bonded species

$$\begin{matrix} X \\ \\ X \end{matrix}\!\!>\!Ga\!-\!Ga\!<\!\!\begin{matrix} X \\ \\ X \end{matrix}$$

in which all three of the gallium valence electrons are bond-forming, and (3) as mixed oxidation state compounds $Ga^+GaX_4^-$, in which the ion Ga^+ (but not GaX_4^-) carries an inert electron pair. The first possibility has been excluded in all cases by the absence of paramagnetism, but instances of (2) and (3) have been established. For example, $GaCl_2$ has been shown to be $Ga^+GaCl_4^-$ in the solid state by X-ray crystallography (13), and in the liquid state by Raman spectroscopy (14), the Raman spectrum showing all the lines expected for a symmetrical tetrahedral species $GaCl_4^-$, and no others.

Similar compounds are gallium "dibromide," $Ga^+GaBr_4^-$ (15), and $Ga^+AlBr_4^-$ (16).

Gallium sulfide GaS, however, is not $Ga^+GaS_2^-$, but has a structure (established (17) by an X-ray diffraction study) in which Ga—Ga bonding is present. The crystal consists of layers in which each gallium is bonded tetrahedrally to three sulfur atoms and to a second gallium:

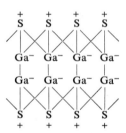

Hence there is no inert pair on the gallium atom. The selenide GaSe (18) and the telluride GaTe (19) are similar.

A number of compounds have been prepared in which various ligands are coordinated to the Ga^+ ion; these include the types $GaL_2^+X^-$, where L is a bidentate ligand like dioxane or dipyridyl; $GaL_4^+X^-$, where L is a monodentate ligand like acetophenone (20, 21, 22); and $Ga(C_6H_6)^+$ $GaCl_4^-$ (23). The existence of complex cations like $Ga\,(dioxane)_2^+$ raises the question as to whether or not the unshared (inert) electron pair on the gallium makes a contribution to the stereochemistry of the ion. There are five electron pairs in the valence shell of the gallium, four of which are donated by the oxygen atoms of the ligand molecules. Ali, Brewer,

Ga—O bonds at right angles to the trigonal plane would be bent in such a way as to give a planar arrangement of four oxygen atoms to one side of the gallium, as in Figure 5.1b. The resulting configuration is then essentially that of a square pyramid. Dyatkina (24) however, preferred to place the unshared valence-shell electron pair in the spherically symmetrical 4s orbital of gallium, in which it is stereochemically inert, and to form the four Ga—O bonds from p^3d hybrid orbitals. The most likely configuration of the hybrids was considered to be square pyramidal, in agreement with the suggestion of Ali et al. However the result of an X-ray diffraction study of Ga(dioxane)$_2$Cl indicates (21) that the arrangement of the Ga—O bonds is that of a slightly distorted trigonal pyramid, with the Ga atom in the center of the base, as shown in Figure 5.1c. The question of the hybrid orbitals used, and the extent of the participation of the gallium 4s^2 pair in them, has therefore not been settled.

In spite of its occurrence in crystals, the Ga$^+$ ion never survives dissolution in water for very long, although there is evidence for its formation as a short-lived species during the anodic oxidation of gallium metal in glacial acetic acid (25). Also, the reaction of gallium metal with hot 11M perchloric acid yields 0.5 mole of H$_2$ gas and 0.25 mole of Cl$^-$ (aq.) for every mole of the ultimate product, Ga^{3+}(aq.). This has been interpreted (26) in terms of the initial formation of Ga$^+$(aq.), followed by immediate oxidation to Ga^{3+}(aq.) by ClO$_4^-$(aq.):

$$Ga + H^+ \rightarrow Ga^+ + \tfrac{1}{2} H_2$$
$$4\,Ga^+ + 8\,H^+ + ClO_4^- \rightarrow 4\,Ga^{3+} + Cl^- + 4\,H_2O$$

C. Indium

In contrast to gallium there are two simple indium halides, InBr (27) and InI (28), whose crystal structures have been determined; there are no In—In bonds, and the two halides therefore contain inert-pair M$^+$ ions. Apart from these examples, indium compounds in low oxidation states are at present not well characterized. Indium monochloride InCl, is a dark red solid of unknown structure (29); In$_2$O has been prepared and gives a distinct X-ray diffraction pattern, and In$_2$S, In$_2$Se, and In$_2$Te have also been reported (30).

The compound InCl$_2$ is of considerable interest because of the possibility of its similarity to the gallium dihalides and its formulation In$^+$

$InCl_4^-$. A phase-rule study (31) has suggested however that $InCl_2$ is in fact a mixture of $InCl_3$ and In_2Cl_3, the latter being the mixed oxidation state compound $(In^+)_3 \, InCl_6^{3-}$. A further phase-rule study established the individuality of the compound $InAlCl_4$, prepared by the reaction

$$2 \, HgCl_2 + In + Al \rightarrow InAlCl_4 + 2 \, Hg$$

but its structure is unknown. On treatment of $InAlCl_4$ with ether, aluminum chloride is removed and a residue of yellow InCl remains. The yellow color of the residue is in contrast to the deep red color of indium monochloride prepared by other (high temperature) methods, and the possibility exists that the two compounds have different crystal structures, but their X-ray diffraction patterns do not seem to have been compared.

As was the case with $Ga^+(aq.)$, the aqueous ion $In^+(aq.)$ is not a stable species, but it has been possible to evaluate the equilibrium constant for the process

$$2 \, In(s) + In^{3+}(aq.) \rightleftharpoons 3 \, In^+(aq.)$$

from a study (32) of In^{III} solutions treated with finely divided metallic indium: $K = 2.4 \times 10^{-11}$.

D. Thallium

Although the trivalent condition is without question the more stable oxidation state for gallium and indium, the reverse is the case for thallium, and the ordinary stable compounds of thallium are in general the monovalent ones. The ion Tl^+ (thallous ion) is stable in aqueous solution, and is not easily oxidized; the standard oxidation potentials

$$In^+(aq.) \rightarrow In^{3+}(aq.) + 2e \qquad E^0 = +0.44 \, \text{volt} \tag{32}$$

and

$$Tl^+(aq.) \rightarrow Tl^{3+}(aq.) + 2e \qquad E^0 = -1.25 \, \text{volt} \tag{33}$$

of which the first is only an estimate, reflect the much greater ease of oxidation of monovalent indium.

All four thallous halides have been examined crystallographically; forms of TlCl, TlBr, and TlI can be obtained with both the rock-salt and cesium chloride structures, while TlF has a deformed rock-salt structure (34).

In addition to the abundant examples of stable monovalent thallium compounds, there are also compounds containing both Tl^I and Tl^{III}, for example TlS (35) and TlSe (36), which can both be formulated $Tl^I(Tl^{III}X_2)$. $TlCl_2$ and Tl_2Cl_3, which are both diamagnetic (37), are presumably $Tl^I(Tl^{III}Cl_4)$ and $(Tl^I)_3(Tl^{III}Cl_6)$ respectively.

A consequence of the stability of monovalent thallium is the difficulty experienced in preparing compounds TlX_3, where X is an easily oxidized radical or anion such as Br^- or I^-; the compound TlI_3 is in fact a polyiodide of monovalent thallium, $Tl^+I_3^-$.

There is one group of compounds in which the relative stability $Tl^I > Tl^{III}$ appears to be reversed. This group comprises the trialkyl and triaryl derivatives $TlR_3(R = CH_3, C_6H_5,$ et cetera) and the dialkyl derivatives TlR_2X (X = Cl, Br, I, NO_3, et cetera). The definite tendency of thallium in these organo-metallic compounds is to use all three of its valence electrons for bonding, there being little evidence for the inert pair effect. For example, trimethyl thallium $Tl(CH_3)_3$ is a reactive compound, but does not readily decompose in the sense

$$Tl^{III}(CH_3)_3 \rightarrow Tl^ICH_3 + CH_3 \cdot CH_3$$

as might have been expected. Its hydrolysis product is $Tl(CH_3)_2OH$, which is a compound of considerable stability and a member of a wide range of stable dialkyl thallium compounds R_2TlX. Some of these latter are ionic, like the iodide $(CH_3)_2TlI$ (cf. the nonexistent $Tl^{III}I_3$), which contains (38) the linear CH_3—Tl^+—CH_3 ion. Indeed no thallium monoalkyl or mono-aryl has yet been isolated; reactions expected to lead to their formation, such as

$$TlCl + C_6H_5Li \rightarrow TlC_6H_5 + LiCl$$

proceed instead (39) in the following way:

$$3\ TlCl + 3\ C_6H_5Li \rightarrow Tl(C_6H_5)_3 + 3\ LiCl + 2\ Tl$$

It is interesting therefore that cyclopentadienyl thallium, $Tl \cdot C_5H_5$, has been prepared (40), but its infrared spectrum suggests a symmetry compatible with a "half-sandwich" structure in which the metal-to-ring bonding is essentially ionic; the presence of a Tl—C sigma bond is improbable.

E. Theoretical Considerations

It is usually assumed that the tendency for the inert pair effect to operate increases as a periodic group is descended. Certainly the effect is most marked in thallium, and hardly apparent at all in boron and aluminum, but it is not so easy to place gallium and indium in the sequence on the basis of the evidence quoted above.

Standard free energies of formation for both monovalent and trivalent compounds of all five elements would enable a decision to be made as to the relative stabilities of the M^I and M^{III} compounds. For example, if it could be demonstrated that the standard free energy change ΔG^0 for a reaction such as

$$MCl_3 \rightarrow MCl + Cl_2 \tag{1}$$

became steadily more negative (or less positive) down the group M = B, Al, Ga, In, Tl, it could be inferred that the stability of the compounds MCl_3 decreased regularly relative to the stability of the compounds MCl, under the standard conditions to which the symbol ΔG^0 refers. If, in addition, structural information were available to establish the presence of an unshared valence-pair in the MCl compounds, it could be further inferred that a tendency to use only one of the three valence electrons increased down the group. To elucidate the problem further, it would then be necessary to consider the energetic factors influencing the magnitude of ΔG^0 for reaction (1). As a first approximation it could be assumed that entropy effects do not influence the *trend* in ΔG^0 down the group. (Evidence to support this assumption is adduced later.) There are then two types of enthalpy cycle which could provide the required information. In the first type (cycle A) an ionic model is adopted for both MCl_3 and MCl, and reaction (1) then becomes the resultant of the following steps:

Cycle A:
   (a) $MCl_3(s) \rightarrow M^{3+}(g) + 3\,Cl^-(g)$
   (b) $2\,Cl^-(g) \rightarrow 2\,Cl(g) + 2e$
   (c) $2\,Cl(g) \rightarrow Cl_2(g)$
   (d) $M^{3+}(g) + 2e \rightarrow M^+(g)$
   (e) $M^+(g) + Cl^-(g) \rightarrow MCl(s)$

in which steps (b) and (c) are independent of M. The factors which tend to make $MCl_3(s)$ unstable with respect to $MCl(s)$ would then be (1) a low lattice enthalpy for MCl_3 (step (a)); (2) high ionization enthalpies for the second and third valence electrons of M (step (d)), and (3) a high lattice enthalpy for MCl (step (e)).

In the second type (cycle B) a molecular (covalent) model is adopted for both MCl_3 and MCl, and again reaction (1) becomes the resultant of a series of steps:

Cycle B:

(f) $MCl_3(s) \rightarrow MCl_3(g)$

(g) $MCl_3(g) \rightarrow M(g) + 3 Cl(g)$

(h) $2 Cl(g) \rightarrow Cl_2(g)$

(i) $M(g) + Cl(g) \rightarrow MCl(g)$

(j) $MCl(g) \rightarrow MCl(s)$

in which step (h) is independent of M. In this case the factors which tend to make MCl_3 unstable with respect to MCl would then be (1) a low heat of sublimation for MCl_3 (step (f)); (2) weak M—Cl bonds, i.e., low $\bar{D}_{M-Cl}$ in the molecule MCl_3 (step (g)); (3) a strong M—Cl bond in the molecule MCl (step (i)) and (4) a high heat of sublimation for MCl (step (j)).

Unfortunately there are insufficient heat data available to make the above rigorous sort of analysis possible for a range of compounds of all five elements, but at least some of the contributing energy terms can be investigated. In particular, it has been suggested (41, 42) that a decrease in the covalent bond strength in the MCl_3 molecule (cycle B, step (g)) is the factor of major importance in determining the trend in stability down the group, and this possibility will now be examined.

1. M—Cl Bond Energies. A measure of the covalent bond strength in the molecule MCl_3 is the mean thermochemical bond energy $\bar{D}_{M-Cl}$, which is one-third of the change in heat content ΔH^0 at $25°C$. accompanying the reaction

$$MCl_3(g) \rightarrow M(g) + 3 Cl(g)$$

The standard heats of formation of all the species in this reaction are known, so $\bar{D}_{M-Cl}$ can be evaluated. The necessary heat data are as follows:

Heats of formation from elements in their standard states,
ΔH_f^0 *(25°C.), kcal./mole*

B(g)	Al(g)	Ga(g)	In(g)	Tl(g)	Cl(g)
135[a]	77.5[b]	65.0[b]	58.2[b]	43[b]	28.94[a]

$BCl_3(g)$	$AlCl_3(g)$	$GaCl_3(s)$	$InCl_3(s)$	$TlCl_3(s)$
−97.1[a]	−137.1[a]	−125.0[c]	−126.0[c]	−84[d]

Heats of sublimation, ΔH^0(25°C.), kcal./mole

GaCl$_3$	InCl$_3$	TlCl$_3$
$\sim 20^c$	$\sim 38^c$	$\sim 19^d$

[a] ref. (43);   [b] Table 1.1;   [c] ref. (44);   [d] ref. (41).

The values of $\bar{D}_{M-Cl}$ calculated from the above are:

B—Cl	Al—Cl	Ga—Cl	In—Cl	Tl—Cl	
106	100	86	78	65	kcal./mole

It is apparent that there is a monotonic decrease in the average strength of the M—Cl covalent bonds in the MCl$_3$(g) molecules in passing down the group.

A measure of the covalent bond strengths in the *monovalent* gaseous chlorides is also available from the bond-dissociation energies. The following values of D_{M-Cl}, the bond-dissociation energy at 0°K., have been selected from Barrow's (45) compilation:

B—Cl	Al—Cl	Ga—Cl	In—Cl	Tl—Cl	
127	117	113	102	90	kcal./mole

These values also decrease down the group, and in each case the M—Cl bond strength in the monochloride is higher than the average bond strength in the trichloride.

If it is assumed that the D_{M-Cl} values at 0°K. for the monochlorides do not differ very much from values of ΔH^0 at 25°C., it is possible to estimate the heat of formation of each MCl(g) species, using the heat data already tabulated; the results of this estimation are:

ΔH_f^0 MCl(g), estimated, kcal./mole

BCl	AlCl	GaCl	InCl	TlCl
+37	−10	−19	−14	−18

If these values are combined with the standard heats of formation of the MCl$_3$(g) species, then the change in heat content ΔH^0 at 25°C. for the reaction

$$MCl_3(g) \rightarrow MCl(g) + Cl_2(g) \qquad (2)$$

is estimated as follows:

$$M = B \qquad \Delta H^0_{\text{reaction (2)}} = +134 \text{ kcal./mole}$$

$$\text{Al} \qquad\qquad\qquad\qquad +127$$
$$\text{Ga} \qquad\qquad\qquad\qquad + 86$$
$$\text{In} \qquad\qquad\qquad\qquad + 74$$
$$\text{Tl} \qquad\qquad\qquad\qquad + 47$$

It appears from these results that, in the gas phase at least, there is a regular increase in the tendency for the MCl_3 molecule to decompose into the monovalent chloride as the group is descended, and that this trend occurs because the bonds in the MCl_3 molecules become progressively weaker and easier to break.

The question to be discussed now is: *Why* do the bond energies decrease down the group?

As discussed in Chapter 1, Section II C the process

$$M(g) + 3 \, Cl(g) \rightarrow MCl_3(g) \qquad\qquad (3)$$

refers to the formation of the molecule MCl_3 from atoms in their *ground states*: In this case the atoms M have s^2p, and the Cl atoms s^2p^5, configurations. The heat evolved in the above process, of which one-third is the mean thermochemical bond energy $\bar{D}_{M-Cl}$, is therefore the resultant of (a) a promotion energy term (the heat necessary to excite the M and Cl atoms to electronic states in which the atomic orbitals are suitably prepared for bond formation), and (b) an intrinsic bond energy term, i.e., the heat evolved when three covalent bonds are formed from the excited atoms:

(a) $M(g) + 3 \, Cl(g) \rightarrow M^*(g) + 3 \, Cl^*(g)$ $\qquad\qquad$ (3a)

(b) $M^*(g) + 3 \, Cl^*(g) \rightarrow MCl_3(g)$ $\qquad\qquad$ (3b)

The overall values of ΔH for reaction (3), calculated from data already quoted, are

BCl_3	$AlCl_3$	$GaCl_3$	$InCl_3$	$TlCl_3$
-319	-301	-257	-233	-195 kcal./mole

and it is clear that the trend in these values (and hence the trend in $\bar{D}_{M-Cl}$) may be due to either promotion energy or intrinsic bond energy factors. The promotion energy data required to evaluate ΔH for step (3a) are not known in all cases, but a guide to the way in which they might be expected to vary down the group can be obtained from information on the spectra of the atoms. The following (46) are the separations between the ground state (s^2p) and the lowest lying $(J = \frac{1}{2})$ excited level of the sp^2 configuration for the atom M:

B	Al	Ga	In	Tl	
28805	29020	37972	34977	45220	cm^{-1}
82.4	83.0	108.5	100.0	129.3	kcal./mole

These figures do not give the energies necessary to promote an s electron to the actual valence state, because in the excited sp^2 state considered, two electrons occupy p orbitals which are mutually perpendicular while the third occupies a spherically symmetrical s orbital; such a set of orbitals could not give rise directly to the observed trigonal disposition of the bonds in the MCl_3 molecules. (For a discussion of valence-state energies, see refs. (42) and (47).) However if it can be assumed that the $s^2p - sp^2$ separations listed above are at least proportional to the ground state $\rightarrow$ valence state promotion energies, then it seems that while there is no regular trend in ΔH for reaction (3a), the promotion of a $6s$ electron in thallium will be a considerably more endothermic process than the corresponding transitions in the other elements of group 3. If the crude assumption is made that the $s^2p - sp^2$ separations are equal to ΔH for reaction (3a), (which also involves the assumption that the Cl atoms do not require excitation before bond-formation), then the heat liberated in reaction (3b), one-third of which is the mean intrinsic bond energy, is as follows:

M =	B	Al	Ga	In	Tl	
$\Delta H_{\text{reaction (3b)}}$	-401	-384	-366	-333	-324	kcal./mole

This result suggests that in spite of the irregular promotion energies, the mean intrinsic M—Cl bond energies decrease down the group, a trend which is presumably a consequence of the increasing diffuseness of the bonding orbitals used for bond formation; poorer overlap, and weaker bonds, result. However it is surprising that the trend should be a regular one in a series in which trends in other fundamental properties such as ionization potentials and electronegativities are anything but regular:

	B	Al	Ga	In	Tl	
1st ionization potential	8.30	5.98	6.00	5.79	6.11	e.v.
2nd ionization potential	25.15	18.82	20.51	18.86	20.42	e.v.
3rd ionization potential	37.92	28.44	30.70	28.03	29.8	e.v.
Electronegativity (48)	2.04	1.61	1.81	1.78	2.04	

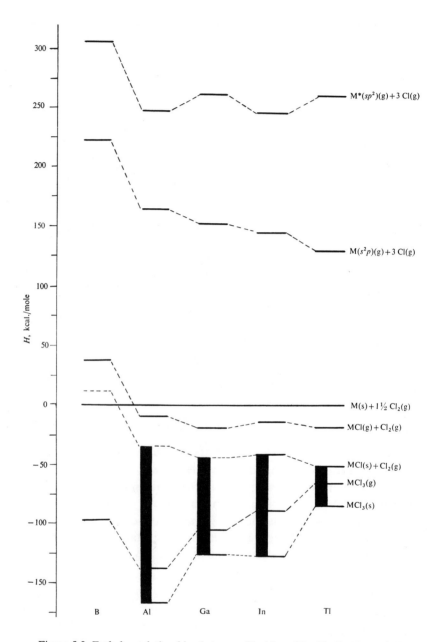

Figure 5.2. Enthalpy relationships between chlorides of B, Al, Ga, In, and Tl.

It is now convenient to summarize the heat quantities evaluated above in a single diagram. Figure 5.2 shows the enthalpies (relative to those of the elements M and Cl_2 in their standard states) of the gaseous trichlorides MCl_3, the gaseous monochlorides MCl, the gaseous ground-state atoms $M + 3$ Cl, and the gas atoms in which M has the excited sp^2 configuration. The enthalpies of the trichlorides in their standard states are also given. In the case of the solid monochlorides, the sublimation energy data necessary to adjust the heats of formation of the gaseous compounds are mostly unknown; for InCl and TlCl the values 27 kcal./mole (41) and 32 kcal./mole (44) have been used. Since it is unlikely that the heats of sublimation will differ significantly, the value 25 kcal./mole has been arbitrarily assigned to BCl, AlCl, and GaCl, and the resulting approximate values of ΔH_f^0 for the solid monochlorides included in Figure 5.2. The significant separations (between $MCl_3(s)$ and $MCl(s)$) are shaded.

The smallest separation is observed for M = thallium, in agreement with the qualitative empirical evidence that the inert pair effect is most marked in this element, and is a consequence of the fact that although the gaseous atoms Tl and 3 Cl are formed most easily (due to the small heat of sublimation of thallium metal), the high energy required to effect the $s^2p \rightarrow sp^2$ transition is not recompensed by a correspondingly high heat evolution on covalent bond formation.

The separations for M = Ga and In are small compared with those for M = B and Al, but it is difficult to decide whether the relative stability of the trivalent state is greater or less for gallium than for indium, in view of the uncertainties in the experimental data. It is interesting that the $s^2p \rightarrow sp^2$ promotion energy is actually lower for indium than for gallium, which partly offsets the effects of the rather weaker covalent bonds formed by indium. For this reason it is conceivable that the inert pair effect may in some cases be more pronounced in gallium than in indium, and that the common assumption that the effect becomes more pronounced as a group is descended may not always be true for the elements of the first and second long periods.

2. Ionic-Model Cycles. It is interesting to approach the decomposition reaction

$$MCl_3(s) \rightarrow MCl(s) + Cl_2(g),$$

using a heat cycle based on an ionic model (cycle A, p. 85), particularly

since it has been found that, on the basis of a covalent model, the covalent bond energy in both the trichlorides and monochlorides decreases
regularly down the group. The question arises as to whether the ionic-
model *lattice energy* shows the same trend.

Lattice enthalpies for the trichlorides MCl_3 (M = Al, Ga, In, Tl),
the monochlorides MCl (M = In, Tl), the trioxides M_2O_3 (M = B, Al,
Ga, In, Tl), and monoxides M_2O (M = Ga, Tl) have been calculated,
using data already given or listed below.

Heats of formation from elements in their standard states,
ΔH_f^0 *(25°C.) kcal./mole*

$AlCl_3(s)$	$B_2O_3(s)$	$Al_2O_3(s)$	$Ga_2O_3(s)$	$In_2O_3(s)$	$Tl_2O_3(s)$
-166.8[b]	-306.1[b]	-400.0[b]	-261[a]	-221.5[b]	-84.5[b]

$Ga_2O(s)$	$Tl_2O(s)$	$O^{2-}(g)$
-82.0[b]	-42.5[b]	217[c]

[a] ref. (49);   [b] ref. (44);   [c] ref. (50).

Lattice enthalpies (kcal./mole)

	$AlCl_3$	$GaCl_3$	$InCl_3$	$TlCl_3$
	1301	1338	1227	1255
			InCl	TlCl
			176	177

B_2O_3	Al_2O_3	Ga_2O_3	In_2O_3	Tl_2O_3
4525	3668	3688	3425	3428
		Ga_2O		Tl_2O
		709		631

Although the data for the monovalent compounds are unfortunately
very sparse, the lattice enthalpies of both the trichlorides MCl_3 and
the trioxides M_2O_3 show, in a broad sense, a general if not very regular
downward trend in passing from boron to thallium. The largest differences occur between boron and aluminum, and again between gallium
and indium; there seems to be very little difference between aluminum
and gallium, or between indium and thallium. On a purely electrostatic
view of the lattice enthalpy, a downward trend in the direction observed
would be expected because the ionic radii of the tripositive ions (51), viz.,

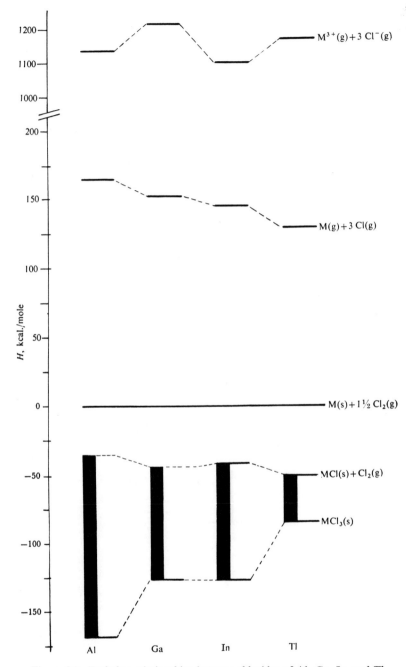

Figure 5.3. Enthalpy relationships between chlorides of Al, Ga, In, and Tl.

93

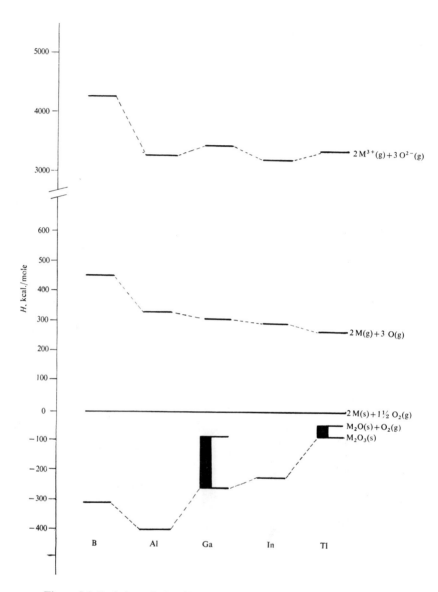

Figure 5.4. Enthalpy relationships between oxides of B, Al, Ga, In, and Tl.

	B^{3+}	Al^{3+}	Ga^{3+}	In^{3+}	Tl^{3+}
$r_M^{3+}(\text{Å})$	0.20	0.50	0.62	0.81	0.95

increase as the group is descended, so that the internuclear distance r in the crystal will tend to increase. The Coulomb attraction between the ions ($z_1 e \cdot z_2 e / r$), and hence the lattice energy, will consequently become smaller. That the lattice enthalpies do not closely follow the ionic radii is presumably due to varying contributions from covalent forces, and to possible inadequacies of the Pauling ionic radii as measures of internuclear distances.

The enthalpy data are summarized in Figure 5.3 for the chlorides and in Figure 5.4 for the oxides. The very small difference in heat content between the trivalent oxide and the monovalent oxide $+O_2$ in the case of

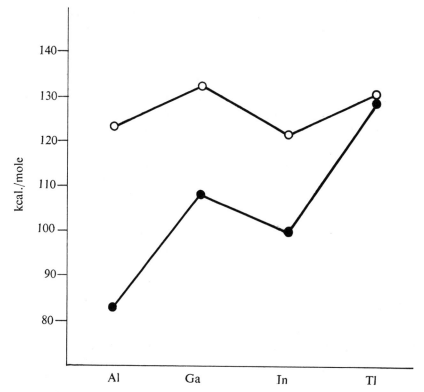

Figure 5.5. Ionization and promotion energies for Al, Ga, In, and Tl.
$O = 0.1 \times \Delta H$ for $M(g) - 3e \rightarrow M^{3+}(g)$; $\bullet = s^2 p \rightarrow sp^2$ separations (spectroscopic).

thallium is very striking, in common with a similar feature in the chloride diagram. The small differences can be attributed to the circumstance that a high expenditure of energy is required to ionize the thallium atom $(M(g) - 3e \rightarrow M^{3+}(g))$, and that this energy term is not offset by a correspondingly high heat evolution (lattice enthalpy) on formation of the crystal from the gaseous ions.

The ionization potentials for the three valence electrons of Al, Ga, In, and Tl show the same irregular trend as the $s^2p \rightarrow sp^2$ promotion energies discussed earlier, and are plotted in Figure 5.5. The increase in both of these quantities which occurs on passing from aluminum to gallium can be traced to the fact that gallium is preceded in atomic number by the first transition series, across which the relatively weak screening power of the $3d$ electrons causes a corresponding increase in the effective nuclear charge acting on the valence electrons in gallium. A similar increase in passing from indium to thallium can be attributed to the interpolation in the third long period of the lanthanide $(4f)$ subshell. Although the ease of formation of the gaseous atoms increases from Al to Tl (following the decreasing heat of sublimation of the elements), the heat of formation of either tripositive ions $M^{3+}(g)$ or of excited atoms $M^*(sp^2)(g)$ is maintained at a fairly constant level by the operation of these effects.

3. Entropy Effects. The factor governing the energetic likelihood of the decomposition

$$MCl_3(s) \rightarrow MCl(s) + Cl_2(g)$$

is of course the accompanying free energy change ΔG^0. In the foregoing discussion only the heat term ΔH has been considered, i.e., any possible effect of the entropy contribution $T \cdot \Delta S$ has not been discussed. For a reaction such as the above, where the states of aggregation do not differ as M changes from B to Tl, it is unlikely that ΔS would differ very much from element to element. It would be expected that in each case the entropy change would be positive (mainly because of the increase in entropy of two chlorines) and hence favor decomposition. An approximate value for ΔS can be obtained by using the known entropy S^0 for $Cl_2(g)$ (53.4 cal. mole/deg.) (33) and known or estimated values of S^0 for the solid chlorides MCl_3 and MCl, using where necessary Latimer's (33) values for the contributions of metals and anions to the absolute entropies of solids. It is found that the term $T \cdot \Delta S$ contributes about 10–12 kcal./mole to the free energy change for the decomposition of the trichlorides, and cannot be responsible for the variation in stability observed down the group.

III. GROUP 4: C, Si, Ge, Sn, Pb

A. General

In this sequence the atoms have ns^2np^2 valence-shell configurations, with four electrons available for bond formation. Divalent compounds stable under ordinary conditions are found only in germanium, tin, and lead. In the case of carbon, molecules such as $CX_2(X = H, F, Cl, Br, I)$ exist only as short-lived species in gas discharge tubes, or as reaction intermediates. In the case of silicon, the monoxide SiO, if it exists in the solid state, is metastable and undoubtedly polymerized (see Chapter 4, Section II A), while SiH_2, $SiCl_2$, et cetera are also polymerized and contain Si—Si bonds rather than unshared electron pairs. In fact, the possibility that apparently divalent compounds MX_2 contain M—M covalent bonds (and hence use all four of their valence electrons for bond formation) is present throughout the entire group: for example, diphenyl tin Ph_2Sn does not consist of discrete molecules carrying unshared tin-atom $5s^2$ electron pairs, but is polymerized through Sn—Sn bonds (52). Satisfactory evidence for true M^{II} derivatives is found for the first time in this group in germanium compounds.

B. Germanium

Divalent compounds which have been reported include GeO, GeS, GeX_2 (X = F, Cl, Br, I), and some complex halides $MGeX_3$. Of these, the crystal structure of GeI_2 has been determined (53); it has a CdI_2 type lattice in which each Ge is surrounded by an octahedron of equidistant iodine atoms, and can therefore be regarded as containing the Ge^{2+} ion (estimated radius 0.98 Å) with an unshared $4s^2$ electron pair, presumably in a spherically symmetrical orbital. There is also some incomplete crystallographic information on the difluoride GeF_2 (54); the germanium has neither tetrahedral (quartzlike) nor octahedral (rutilelike) coordination. In view of the volatility (m.p. 110°C.; distils in vacuo at 130°C.) and solubility of the compound, it has been suggested that its structure is pseudotetrahedral, each Ge being surrounded by three F atoms, with the nonbonding (inert) electron pair occupying the fourth tetrahedral position. This arrangement would give rise to a chain-type structure like that of selenium dioxide:

$$
\begin{array}{ccccccc}
F & & F & & F & & F \\
\diagdown & \diagup & \diagdown & \diagup & \diagdown & \diagup & \diagdown \\
& \overset{..}{Ge} & & \overset{..}{Ge} & & \overset{..}{Ge} & \\
& | & & | & & | & \\
& F & & F & & F &
\end{array}
$$

If this is the case the inert pair is stereochemically active, and is not confined to the spherically symmetrical germanium $4s$ orbital. Also, the complex fluoride $CsGeF_3$ (55) does not have a perovskite structure like $KZnF_3$, presumably because the unshared pair on the germanium atom contributes to the stereochemistry. The presence of the inert electron pair is thus well-established in germanium, although it is by no means always stereochemically inert.

C. Tin

Compounds of divalent tin are too well-known to require detailed description; the tetravalent condition is however still the more stable in the sense that Sn^{II} compounds are easily oxidized, and reagents such as oxygen and the halogens yield the Sn^{IV} compound directly on reaction with tin metal. Unlike the Ge^{2+} ion, the stannous ion Sn^{2+} survives dissolution in water.

In many Sn^{II} compounds, the stereochemistry is such as to suggest strongly that the inert electron pair is stereochemically active and not confined to the tin atom $5s$ orbital. Examples include the following.

1. SnO. The structure of this oxide has been determined by X-ray diffraction by Moore and Pauling (56). Each tin atom is bonded to four oxygens which are arranged in a square on one side of the tin atom; each of the oxygen atoms is linked to a tetrahedron of tin atoms. This arrangement implies the presence of the inert pair in a hybrid orbital at the apex of the SnO_4 pyramid:

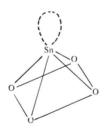

2. $SnCl_2 \cdot 2H_2O$. This crystal contains layers of pyramidal ($SnCl_2 H_2O$) units (57), with the lone electron pair presumably at the apex:

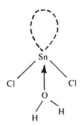

3. $K_2SnCl_4 \cdot H_2O$. An early and incomplete X-ray diffraction study of this compound claimed (58) the presence of infinite chains of octa-hedral $SnCl_6$ groups, in which each octahedron shared two opposite edges. However a more recent study (59) has established that the compound is better formulated $KCl \cdot KSnCl_3 \cdot H_2O$, since it contains pyra-midal $SnCl_3^-$ ions (again with the inert pair assigned to a hybrid orbital at the apex of the pyramid), together with isolated K^+ and Cl^- ions. Pyramidal species $SnCl_3^-$ and $SnBr_3^-$ have also been identified by Raman spectroscopy (60) in ether solutions.

4. Gaseous Dihalides. $SnCl_2$, $SnBr_2$, and SnI_2 have been studied by electron diffraction (61) and have been found to form nonlinear molecules. This result, together with the structures described above, are in accord with Sidgwick and Powell's view (62) that valence-shell elec-tron pairs, both bonding and nonbonding, adopt positions which mini-mize the repulsions between them. Accordingly, a molecule $SnCl_2$, in which there are two bonding pairs and one nonbonding pair surrounding the tin atom, adopts a bent configuration in contrast to the linear arrangement found in mercuric chloride $HgCl_2$, in which there is no nonbonding pair. The evidence is not conclusive however, since in $SnCl_2$ a tin atom with configuration $5s^2 \, 5p_x^1 \, 5p_y^1$ could conceivably form two covalent bonds with the $5p$ orbitals, giving two Sn—Cl bonds at right angles, and the $5s^2$ pair stereochemically inert.

The Sidgwick-Powell theory has been reviewed by Gillespie and Nyholm (63), and a discussion of the stereochemical activity of the inert pair in these compounds has been given by Dunitz and Orgel (64) and by Orgel (65); the crystal chemistry of divalent tin has been described by Rundle and Olson (66).

D. Lead

The inert pair effect is most marked with lead, as it is with ~~gallium~~ *Thallium* in group 3. The tetravalent state in lead is easily reduced to the more stable divalent condition, and compounds derived from Pb^{IV} (e.g., PbO_2) are strong oxidizing agents. In contrast to tin, compounds like PbO_2 and $PbCl_4$ cannot be prepared by direct union of the elements, and Pb^{IV} derivatives of easily oxidized anions like Br^- and I^- have not been prepared. The same curious reversal of stability is found in the organo-lead compounds as was discussed earlier for thallium: Although there is an extensive chemistry of Pb^{IV} alkyls and aryls, organo-derivatives of Pb^{II} are few in number and difficult to prepare. The preferential formation of Pb^{IV} alkyls is well illustrated by the fact that $Pb(CH_3)_4$ is formed from the chloride of *divalent* lead, $PbCl_2$, and a Grignard reagent:

$$4 \; CH_3MgI + 2 \; PbCl_2 \rightarrow Pb(CH_3)_4 + Pb + 2 \; MgCl_2 + 2 \; MgI_2$$

Pb^{II} (plumbous) compounds are familiar and of widespread occurrence; the Pb^{2+} ion is present in many crystals and can be prepared under aqueous conditions. The geometry of the crystalline compounds (which have much in common with those of Sn^{II}) and the problem of the stereochemical significance of the inert pair are discussed in refs. (34) and (64).

E. Theoretical Considerations

The decrease in covalent bond strength discussed in Section II for the group 3 elements is found again in group 4. The following are mean thermochemical bond energies $\bar{D}_{M-Cl}$, $\bar{D}_{M-H}$, and $\bar{D}_{M-C}$ calculated from the heat data shown for M^{IV} compounds.

Heats of formation from elements in their standard states,
ΔH_f^0 *(25°C.), kcal./mole*

C(g)	Si(g)	Ge(g)	Sn(g)	Pb(g)	Cl(g)	H(g)	O^{2-}(g)
170.9[a]	108[a]	89[b]	72.0[a]	46.8[a]	28.94[a]	52.09[a]	217[f]

CCl_4(g)	$SiCl_4$(g)	$GeCl_4$(l)	$SnCl_4$(g)	$PbCl_4$(l)	$SnCl_2$(s)	$PbCl_2$(s)
−25.5[a]	−150[a]	−130[d]	−117.9[a]	−78.9[d]	−83.6[c]	−85.8[c]

CH_4(g)	SiH_4(g)	GeH_4(g)	SnH_4(g)
−17.9[a]	+7.3[g]	+21.6[g]	+38.9[g]

SiO$_2$ (quartz)	GeO$_2$(s)	SnO$_2$(s)	PbO$_2$(s)	GeO(s)	SnO(s)	PbO(s)
-209.9[a]	-128.3[e]	-138.8[e]	-66.1[c]	-73[k]	-68.4[c]	-52.5[a]

C(CH$_3$)$_4$(g)	Si(CH$_3$)$_4$(g)	Ge(CH$_3$)$_4$(g)	Sn(CH$_3$)$_4$(g)	Pb(CH$_3$)$_4$(g)
-39.7	-63[h]	-35[i]	-13.6[e]	$+32.6$[j]

Heats of vaporization, $\Delta H^0_{vap.}$ (25°C.) kcal./mole

CCl$_4$	SiCl$_4$	GeCl$_4$	SnCl$_4$	PbCl$_4$
7.88[c]	7.2[c]	8.1[d]	9.3[c]	9[d]

[a] ref. (43); [b] ref. (67); [c] ref. (44); [d] ref. (41); [e] ref. (68); [f] ref. (50);
[g] ref. (69); [h] ref. (70); [i] ref. (71); [j] ref. (72); [k] ref. (33).

Thermochemical bond energies, $\bar{D}$, kcal./mole

Bond	M = C	Si	Ge	Sn	Pb
M—Cl in MCl$_4$	78	94	82	77	58
M—H in MH$_4$	99	77	69	60	—
M—C in M(CH$_3$)$_4$	83	73	61	52	34

($\bar{D}_{C-H}$ assumed to be 90 kcal./mole.)

In all three cases (M—Cl, M—H, and M—C) there is a regular decrease in bond energy down the group C, Si, Ge, Sn, Pb (with the solitary exception of C—Cl in the M—Cl sequence). The result of the diminishing bond energy in the chlorides is the formation of divalent compounds in which, presumably, the expenditure of energy on the promotion of an electron of the s^2 pair is either avoided or minimized. It is curious that, although the M—H and M—C bond energies show the same trend, there is little indication that either divalent hydrides or divalent alkyls are formed preferentially, even by lead.

In the case of the dioxides MO$_2$ (M = Si, Ge, Sn, Pb) and the monoxides MO (M = Ge, Sn, Pb) available heats of formation permit the calculation of the following lattice enthalpies:

SiO$_2$	GeO$_2$	SnO$_2$	PbO$_2$	
3135	3048	2799	2782	kcal./mole

	GeO	SnO	PbO	
	931	867	838	kcal./mole

Both series show a general downward trend.

It is now possible to construct enthalpy diagrams like those for the group 3 chlorides and oxides. For this purpose a measure of the promotion energies for the process

$$M(s^2p^2)(g) \rightarrow M^*(sp^3)(g)$$

is required, and the following figures have been calculated from atomic spectra data (46) for the separations between the ground s^2p^2 state and the lowest-lying excited level of the sp^3 configuration:

C	Si	Ge	Sn	Pb	
96.5	95.3	119.9	113.3	~145	kcal./mole

(The required spectroscopic data were not available for lead; the approximate figure ~145 kcal./mole is the result of a rough extrapolation

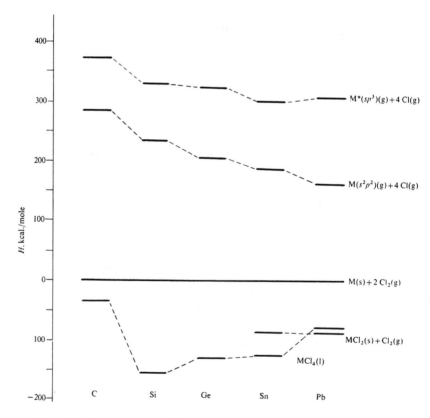

Figure 5.6. Enthalpy relationships between chlorides of C, Si, Ge, Sn, and Pb.

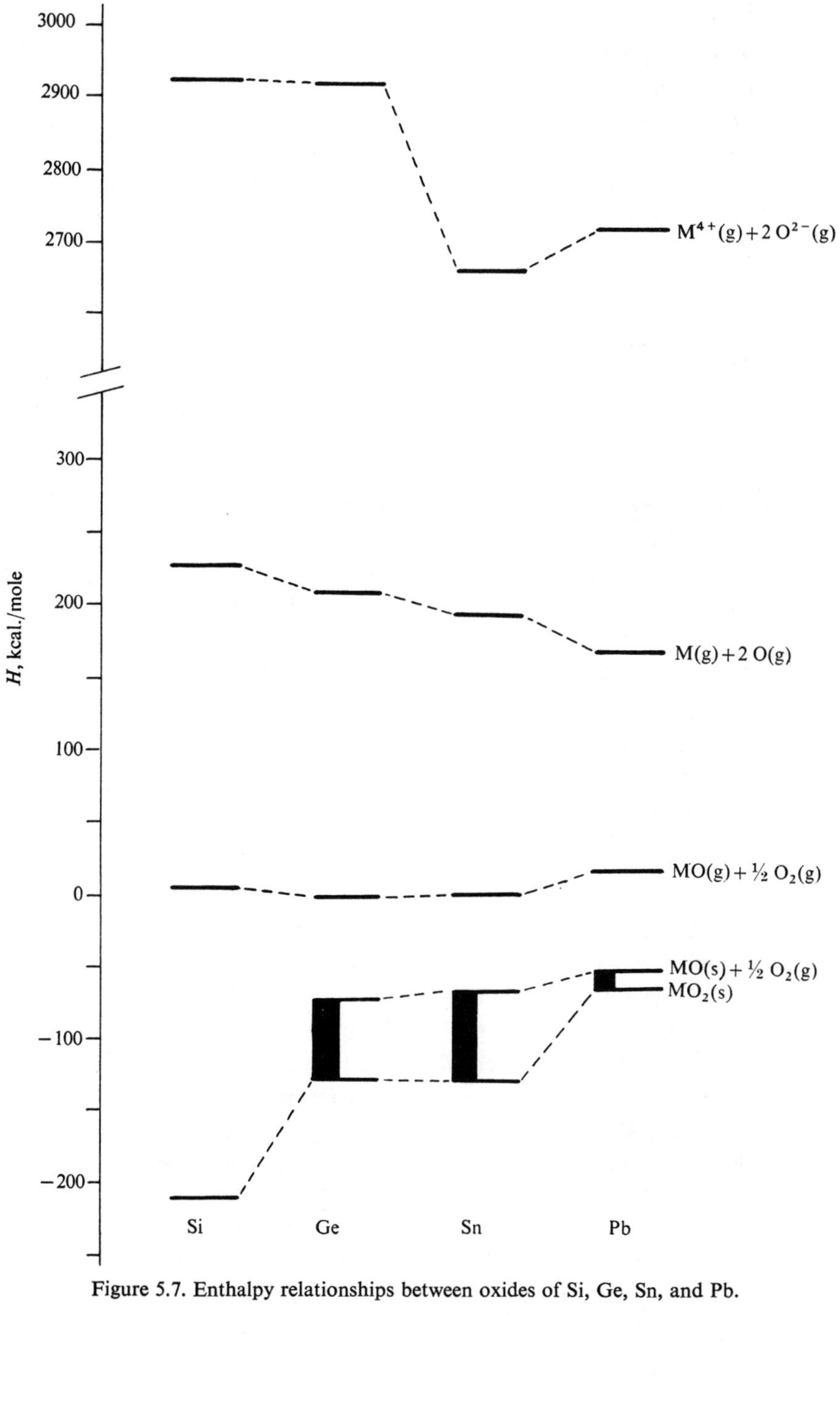

Figure 5.7. Enthalpy relationships between oxides of Si, Ge, Sn, and Pb.

based on the observed promotion energies in Zn, Cd, and Hg and in Ga, In, and Tl.)

The heats of formation of the gaseous oxides MO(g) were estimated approximately from the spectroscopic bond-dissociation energies listed by Cottrell (67); in view of the uncertainty in many of the values, they were not corrected to values of ΔH at 25°C.:

	SiO(g)	GeO(g)	SnO(g)	PbO(g)
D_{M-O}, kcal./mole	165	150	132	94
$-\Delta H_f^0$, kcal./mole	+3	−1	0	+13

The two diagrams (Figures 5.6 and 5.7) show the same broad features as the corresponding diagrams for the group 3 elements. The small separations between the tetravalent and divalent compounds of lead is again a consequence of the fact that the $s^2p^2 \rightarrow sp^3$ promotion energy or the $M(g) \rightarrow M^{3+}(g)$ ionization energy is not offset by correspondingly high bond energies or lattice energies. The rather scanty data for Ge^{II} compounds make a comparison between germanium and tin difficult, but in the case of the oxides (Figure 5.7) there seems to be little difference between the two elements with respect to the relative stabilities of the M^{IV} and M^{II} oxidation states.

IV. GROUP 5: N, P, As, Sb, Bi

A. General

These elements have ns^2np^3 valence-shell configurations. An inert pair effect comparable to that discussed in the preceding groups 3 and 4 is more difficult to discern in this group since all the atoms can achieve a a closed-shell octet (noble gas) configuration by using only three of their five valence electrons for covalent-bond formation, and this will undoubtedly exert a powerful influence on their reactivity. For example, familiar molecules like NH_3 and PCl_3 contain an unshared electron pair in the valence shell of the central atom, and this pair is not "inert" in the usual sense; however in an ion like Bi^{3+} there is no obvious reason (like the achievement of a valence octet) for the use of only three of the five valence electrons, and the presence of the unshared $6s^2$ pair in Bi^{3+} is usually ascribed to the operation of the "inert pair effect." It is still of interest, of course, to examine the stability of the 5-covalent compounds MX_5.

B. M^{3+} Ions

The existence of salts like $Sb_2(SO_4)_3$, $Sb(NO_3)_3$, $Bi_2(SO_4)_3$, $Bi(NO_3)_3$, and $Bi(ClO_4)_3$ suggests that Sb^{3+} and Bi^{3+} ions are present in the crystals; however in the absence of structural information it is impossible to decide whether or not the s^2 electron pair has any influence on the crystal geometry. Similar salts of arsenic have not been prepared.

Halide complexes such as $(CH_3NH_3^+) AsCl_4^-$, $KSbF_4$, K_2SbCl_5, $KBiF_4$, K_2BiF_5, and K_3BiF_6 are known, and in the cases which have been examined by X-ray diffraction the presence of the unshared electron pair seems always to affect the stereochemistry. For example, in $(NH_4)_2SbCl_5$ each Sb is surrounded by five Cl atoms at five of the apices of an octahedron (73); the unshared pair presumably occupies the sixth position.

C. MX_5 Compounds

In this group the formation of five-covalent molecules MX_5, in which all five valence electrons are engaged in the formation of bonds to five other atoms, is subject to the influence of at least two effects which have not been considered in the groups already discussed.

(1) The first-row atom nitrogen does not form NX_5 molecules because of the unavailability of suitable low-energy orbitals to accommodate all five electron pairs — nitrogen cannot "expand its octet" (see Chapter 2).

(2) Arsenic, the first long period element, shows a reluctance to form AsX_5 molecules (e.g., $AsCl_5$ has never been prepared, whereas PCl_5 and $SbCl_5$ are both well-known) for reasons which are discussed in Chapter 6. Consequently, the stability relationship between the M^V and M^{III} states shows a very irregular trend in passing down the group; empirical evidence makes it clear that M^V compounds are very unstable where $M = Bi$, and the elements exhibiting the most stable MX_5 compounds are therefore phosphorus and antimony.

There is a serious lack of thermodynamic data for compounds in this group. The only complete series of compounds which might provide covalent bond strength information are the fluorides, which exist for all five elements in the case of the trifluorides (MF_3), and for all except nitrogen in the case of the pentafluorides. Unfortunately, too few heat and free energy data are available to permit a comprehensive analysis.

There is little doubt however as to the low stability of Bi^V compounds. The only pentahalide of bismuth is BiF_5, which is a powerful fluorinating agent and easily reduced, while the oxide Bi_2O_5 and the derived bismuthates $MBiO_3$ are not well-characterized and are very strong oxidizing agents. Presumably the Bi^V—X bond strength is too low in most cases to provide the energy required for promotion of one of the $6s^2$ pair of electrons, and Bi^{III} compounds are therefore formed preferentially, thus constituting a parallel to the stability of Pb^{II} and Tl^I in the preceding groups.

V. MERCURY

It is sometimes considered, for example by Sidgwick (74) and by Cotton and Wilkinson (75), that the first signs of the inert pair effect are found in mercury, because many mercury compounds readily decompose to give metallic mercury, which forms a monatomic vapor at moderate temperatures; this is regarded as evidence for a tendency on the part of mercury to behave as though its $6s^2$ valence electron pair were unreactive. Certainly the empirical evidence suggests that nonvalent mercury (i.e., the element itself) shows the same sort of stability as that manifested by Tl^I, Pb^{II}, and Bi^{III} in the succeeding groups. It is therefore of interest to make the same thermodynamic analysis of Zn, Cd, and Hg compounds as was made for the elements of groups 3 and 4; the analysis is greatly facilitated by the circumstance that the lower valence state of Zn, Cd, and Hg may be regarded as the gaseous element itself.

Heats of formation from elements in their standard states, ΔH_f^0 (25°C.) kcal./mole.

	Fluoride	Chloride	Bromide	Iodide	Oxide	Sulfide
Solid:						
Zn	−176.0	−99.6	−78.4	−49.8	−83.2[a]	−48.5[a]
Cd	−164.9	−93.0	−75.8	−48.4	−61.1[b]	−34.5[b]
Hg	−105	−53.4	−40.7	−25.3	−21.7[b]	−13.9[b]

	Fluoride	Chloride	Bromide	Iodide
Gas:				
Zn	-115	-68	-47.4	-18
Cd	-89	-50	-36.8	-13.4
Hg	-72	-33.4	-20.7	-3.5

Zn(g)	Cd(g)	Hg(g)	F(g)	Cl(g)	Br(g)	I(g)	O(g)	S(g)
30^c	26.5^c	14.66^c	18.9^a	28.94^a	26.76^a	25.52^a	59.6^a	66.4^a

Electron affinities, ΔH for $(25°C.)$ $X + ne \rightarrow X^{n-}$, kcal./mole

F	Cl	Br	I	O(2e)	S(2e)
-83.5^d	-87.3^d	-82.0^d	-75.7^d	$+157^e$	$+86^e$

[a] ref. (43); [b] ref. (44); [c] Table 1.1; [d] Chapter 1, p. 12; [e] from $\Delta H_f^0 X^{2-}(g)$ values quoted in ref. (50) combined with $\Delta H_f^0 X(g)$ values from Table 1.3.

All data for the solid and gaseous dihalides are from ref. (76).

Measures of the promotion energies for the process

$$M(s^2)(g) \rightarrow M(s^1 p^1)(g)$$

were obtained from spectroscopic data (46):

	Zn	Cd	Hg	
	92.5	86.2	107.6	kcal./mole

The following lattice enthalpies and mean thermochemical bond energies have been calculated from the above data:

Lattice enthalpies.

Values of $\Delta H(25°C.)$ for $MX_2(s) \rightarrow M^{2+}(g) + 2 X^-(g)$, $X = F$, Cl, Br, I; or $MY(s) \rightarrow M^{2+}(g) + Y^{2-}(g)$, $Y = O$, S. kcal./mole.

ZnF_2	$ZnCl_2$	$ZnBr_2$	ZnI_2	ZnO	ZnS
711	647	632	614	964	865

CdF_2	$CdCl_2$	$CdBr_2$	CdI_2	CdO	CdS
662	603	592	574	905	813

HgF_2	$HgCl_2$	$HgBr_2$	HgI_2	HgO	HgS
667	627	621	615	929	857

Mean thermochemical bond energies.

One-half of ΔH(25°C.) for $MX_2(g) \rightarrow M(g) + 2\ X(g)$, kcal./mole.

	$\bar{D}_{M-F}$	$\bar{D}_{M-Cl}$	$\bar{D}_{M-Br}$	$\bar{D}_{M-I}$
M = Zn	91	78	66	50
Cd	77	67	58	46
Hg	62	53	45	35

The principal thermochemical features of the halides, oxides, and sulfides of zinc, cadmium, and mercury are summarized in Figures 5.8, 5.9, and 5.10.

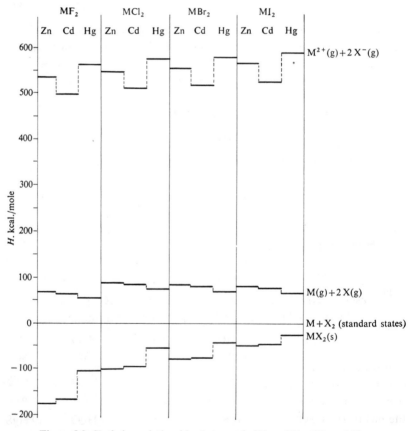

Figure 5.8. Enthalpy relationships between halides of Zn, Cd, and Hg.

It can be seen that in all cases the solid compounds, and also the gaseous halides, become progressively less stable with respect to the elements in passing from zinc to mercury. In general there is only a small difference between zinc and cadmium compounds in this respect, and a much larger one between cadmium and mercury. This is the same feature as was observed in the cases of groups 3 and 4 already discussed; for example, gallium^{III} and indium^{III} compounds have roughly similar stabilities with respect to the lower (M^I) oxidation state, while in the case of thallium the difference in stability is much more marked.

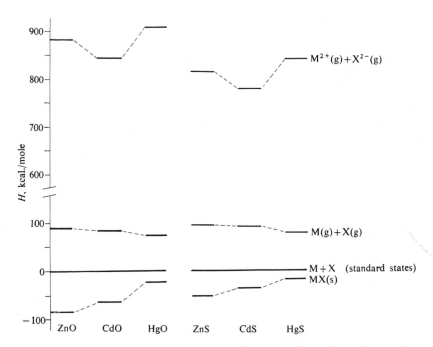

Figure 5.9. Enthalpy relationships between oxides and sulfides of Zn, Cd, and Hg.

It is not difficult to trace the cause of this trend. The constituent gaseous ground-state atoms are formed with decreasing heat absorption from zinc to mercury, following the decrease in heat of sublimation of the metal. However, the readiness with which either the gas-phase ions, or the gas-phase atoms in which the ground state s^2 configuration of the metal atom has been excited to the s^1p^1 configuration, are formed does not show a regular trend: there is a marked decrease in the heat required in passing from zinc to cadmium, and a marked increase in passing from cadmium to mercury. The decrease between zinc and cadmium is a con-

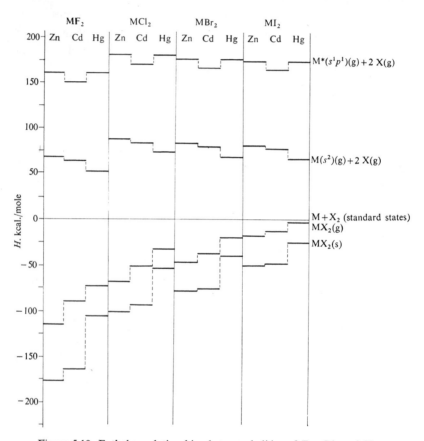

Figure 5.10. Enthalpy relationships between halides of Zn, Cd, and Hg.

sequence of the lower ionization potentials and $s^2 \rightarrow s^1p^1$ excitation energy of the cadmium atom, and the increase between cadmium and mercury is a consequence of, and the higher values of these quantities caused by, the presence of the lanthanide ($4f$) elements in the third long period.

The lattice enthalpies always decrease from zinc to cadmium (because of the bigger internuclear distances in the cadmium compounds), but rise again in the mercury compounds; the Pauling ionic radii (51), $Cd^{2+} = 0.97$ Å and $Hg^{2+} = 1.10$ Å, suggest that internuclear distances should be larger (and lattice enthalpies smaller) in the mercury compounds, but obviously covalent forces play a large part in determining the crystal energies of many mercury compounds (e.g., $HgCl_2$ has a molecular lattice) and predictions based on a simple ionic model are unreliable. The lattice enthalpies of the mercury compounds are not however sufficiently high to outweigh the effect of the large ionization potentials of mercury, and the net result is a relatively low heat of formation of each solid compound.

The mean thermochemical bond energies, unlike the lattice enthalpies, decrease uniformly from zinc to mercury, and again the relatively low heats of formation of the mercury halides can be attributed to the fact that the high $s^2 \rightarrow s^1p^1$ promotion energy is not offset by a correspondingly high covalent bond energy.

In this connection it is interesting that Orgel (77) has suggested that the mercury atom, because of the comparatively large $6s - 6p$ separation, may prefer to use ds rather than sp hybrids for covalent bond formation in 2-covalent compounds. The $5d - 6s$ separation, in contrast to the $6s - 6p$ separation, is considerably less in Hg than in Cd, and it is suggested that, in the $HgCl_2$ molecule, for example, the mercury atom uses one ds hybrid and one p orbital for the formation of two linear covalent bonds.

A case in which the regular decrease in stability with respect to the elements in their standard states along the series Zn, Cd, Hg is not observed is that of the gaseous dimethyl derivatives, whose heats of formation (68) are

$Zn(CH_3)_2(g)$	$Cd(CH_3)_2(g)$	$Hg(CH_3)_2(g)$	
$+13.3$	$+28.1$	$+22.4$	kcal./mole

from which it is apparent that the mercury compound is rather *more* stable than the cadmium derivative. The mean thermochemical bond energies $\bar{D}_{M-C}$ for the metal-to-carbon bonds, calculated on the assumption that $\bar{D}_{C-H} = 98.8$ kcal./mole, are

Zn—C	Cd—C	Hg—C	
39.1	30.5	27.4	kcal./mole

and these decrease in the usual way. These results emphasize that the heat of formation of each compound discussed represents a relatively small difference between large contributing energy terms, and that while a good deal of regularity may be discernible in these contributing terms, the same regularity may not be maintained in a small difference between them.

To summarize, the inert pair effect is most pronounced in the heaviest member of each group and is a result of a relatively less favorable balance between the energy required to remove or excite one of the s^2 electrons on the one hand, and the energy recovered on ionic-lattice or covalent molecule formation on the other. The high ionization and promotion energies observed for the heaviest group member are apparently due to the presence of the lanthanide $(4f)$ elements in the third long period. There is insufficient evidence to decide whether the trend down an entire group is *consistently* towards a diminishing stability of the higher or group valence state, for in passing from gallium to indium, or from germanium to tin, the effect of a lower bond-energy or lattice energy in In^{III} and Sn^{IV} compounds is partly offset by the fact that ionization and promotion energies for In and Sn are actually lower than those for Ga and Ge. In general, there does not seem to be a very big difference between the members of the first long period (Zn, Ga, Ge) and those of the second (Cd, In, Sn) in respect to the relative stabilities of the lower and higher oxidation states.

REFERENCES

(1) Sidgwick, N. V., *Ann. Rept. Progr. Chem. (Chem. Soc. London)*, **20**, 120 (1933).
(2) Grimm, H. G., and A. Sommerfeld, *Z. Physik*, **36**, 36 (1926).
(3) Afoji, M., and W. N. Lipscomb, *Acta Cryst.*, **6**, 547 (1953).
(4) Jacobson, R. A., and W. N. Lipscomb, *J. Chem. Phys.*, **31**, 605 (1959).
(5) Klemm, W., and E. Voss, *Z. Anorg. Allgem. Chem.*, **251**, 233 (1943).
(6) Raijola, E., and A. W. Davidson, *J. Am. Chem. Soc.*, **78**, 556 (1956).
(7) Greenwood, N. N., in H. J. Emeleus and A. G. Sharpe, eds., *Advances in Inorganic Chemistry and Radiochemistry*, Vol. 5, Academic Press, Inc., New York, 1963, p. 91.
(8) Gastinger, E., *Naturwissenschaften*, **42**, 95 (1955).
(9) Spandau, H., and F. Klanberg, *Z. Anorg. Allgem. Chem.*, **295**, 300 (1958).

(10) Kotovich, V. A., quoted in (7).

(11) Gastinger, E., *Angew. Chem.*, **67**, 108 (1955).

(12) Corbett, J. D., and R. K. McMullen, *J. Am. Chem. Soc.*, **77**, 4217 (1955).

(13) Garton, G., and H. M. Powell, *J. Inorg. Nucl. Chem.*, **4**, 84 (1957).

(14) Woodward, L. A., G. Garton, and H. L. Roberts, *J. Chem. Soc.*, **1956**, 3723.

(15) Woodward, L. A., N. N. Greenwood, J. R. Hall, and I. J. Worrall, *J. Chem. Soc.*, **1958**, 1505.

(16) Corbett, J. D., and A. Hershaft, *J. Am. Chem. Soc.*, **80**, 1530 (1958).

(17) Hahn, H., and G. Frank., *Z. Anorg. Allgem. Chem.*, **278**, 333, 340 (1955).

(18) Schubert, K., and E. Dörre, *Naturwissenschaften*, **40**, 604 (1953).

(19) Schubert, K., E. Dörre, and E. Günzel, *Naturwissenschaften*, **41**, 448 (1953).

(20) Ali, S. M., F. M. Brewer, J. R. Chadwick, and G. Garton, *J. Inorg. Nucl. Chem.*, **9**, 124 (1959).

(21) Brewer, F. M., J. R. Chadwick, and G. Garton, *J. Inorg. Nucl. Chem.*, **23**, 45 (1961).

(22) Brewer, F. M., G. Garton, and D. M. L. Goodgame, *J. Inorg. Nucl. Chem.*, **9**, 56 (1959).

(23) Rundle, R. E., and J. D. Corbett, *J. Am. Chem. Soc.*, **79**, 757 (1957).

(24) Dyatkina, M. E., *Russ. J. Inorg. Chem. (English Transl.)*, 1309 (1959).

(25) Davidson, A. W., and F. Jirik, *J. Am. Chem. Soc.*, **72**, 1700 (1950).

(26) Schlug, K., and A. Sadowski, *J. Am. Chem. Soc.*, **83**, 3538 (1961).

(27) Stephenson, N. C., and D. P. Mellor, *Australian J. Sci. Res.*, **A3**, 581 (1950).

(28) Jones, R. E., and D. H. Templeton, *Acta Cryst.*, **8**, 847 (1955).

(29) Gastinger, E., *Angew. Chem.*, **67**, 103 (1955).

(30) Klemm, W., and H. U. von Vogel, *Z. Anorg. Allgem. Chem.*, **219**, 45 (1934).

(31) Clark, R. J., E. Griswold, and J. Kleinberg, *J. Am. Chem. Soc.*, **80**, 4764 (1958).

(32) Helper, L. G., Z Z. Hugus, and W. M. Latimer, *J. Am. Chem. Soc.*, **75**, 5652 (1953).

(33) Latimer, W. M., *Oxidation Potentials*, 2nd ed., Prentice-Hall, Inc., New York, 1952.

(34) Wells, A. F., *Structural Inorganic Chemistry*, 3rd ed., Oxford University Press, London, 1962.

(35) Fielding, P., G. Fischer, and E. Mooser, *Phys. Chem. Solids*, **8**, 434 (1959).

(36) Ketelaar, J. A. A., *Z. Krist.*, **101**, 396 (1939).

(37) Meier, D. J., and C. S. Garner, *J. Chem. Phys.*, **18**, 237 (1950).

(38) Powell, H. M., and D. M. Crowfoot, *Z. Krist.*, **87**, 370 (1934).

(39) Gilman, H., and R. G. Jones, *J. Am. Chem. Soc.*, **61**, 1513 (1939); **62** 2357 (1940).

(40) Cotton, F. A., and L. T. Reynolds, *J. Am. Chem. Soc.*, **80**, 269 (1958).

(41) Drago, R. S., *J. Phys. Chem.*, **62**, 353 (1958).

(42) Cotton, F. A., and G. Wilkinson, *Advanced Inorganic Chemistry*, Interscience, New York, 1962, p. 349.

(43) Lewis, G. N., and M. Randall, *Thermodynamics*, revised by K. S. Pitzer and L. Brewer, 2nd ed., McGraw-Hill, New York, 1961.

(44) Kubaschewski, O., and E. L. Evans, *Metallurgical Thermochemistry*, Pergamon Press Ltd., London, 1956.

(45) Barrow, R. F., *Trans. Faraday Soc.*, **56**, 952 (1960).

(46) Moore, C. E., *"Atomic Energy Levels," Nat. Bur. Std. (U.S.) Circ.* **467**, Vol. 1 (1949), Vol. 2 (1952), Vol. 3 (1958).

(47) Coulson, C. A., *Valence*, Oxford University Press, London, 1952.

(48) Allred, A. L., *J. Inorg. Nucl. Chem.*, **17**, 215 (1961).

(49) Cochran, C. N., and L. M. Foster, *J. Electrochem. Soc.*, **109**, 144 (1962).

(50) Waddington, T. C., in H. J. Emeleus and A. G. Sharpe, eds., *Advances in Inorganic Chemistry and Radiochemistry*, Vol. 1, Academic Press, Inc. New York 1959, p. 157.

(51) Pauling, L., *The Nature of the Chemical Bond*, 3rd ed., Cornell University Press, New York, 1960.

(52) Olson, D. H., and R. E. Rundle, *Inorg. Chem.*, **2**, 1310 (1963).

(53) Powell, H. M., and F. M. Brewer, *J. Chem. Soc.*, **1938**, 197.

(54) Bartlett, N., and K. C. Yu, *Can. J. Chem.*, **39**, 80 (1961).

(55) Muetterties, E. L., *Inorg. Chem.*, **1**, 342 (1962).

(56) Moore, W. J., and L. Pauling, *J. Am. Chem. Soc.*, **63**, 1392 (1941).

(57) Kamenar, B., and D. Grdenic, *J. Chem. Soc.*, **1961**, 3954.

(58) Brasseur, H., and A. de Rassenfosse, *Z. Krist.*, **101**, 389 (1939).

(59) Grdenic, D., and B. Kamenar, *Proc. Chem. Soc.*, 304 (1961); *J. Inorg. Nucl. Chem.*, **24**, 1039 (1962).

(60) Woodward, L. A., and M. J. Taylor, *J. Chem. Soc.*, **1962**, 407.

(61) Lister, M. W., and L. E. Sutton, *Trans. Faraday, Soc.*, **37**, 406 (1941)

(62) Sidgwick, N. V., and H. M. Powell, *Proc. Roy. Soc., London*, **A176**, 153 (1940).

(63) Gillespie, R. J., and R. S. Nyholm, *Quart. Rev. (London)*, **11**, 339 (1957).

(64) Dunitz, J. D., and L. E. Orgel, in H. J. Emeleus and A. G. Sharpe, eds., *Advances in Inorganic Chemistry and Radiochemistry*, Vol. 2, Academic Press, Inc., New York, 1960, p. 1.

(65) Orgel, L. E., *J. Chem. Soc.*, **1959**, 3815.

(66) Rundle, R. E., and D. H. Olson, *Inorg. Chem.*, **3**, 596 (1964).

(67) Cottrell, T. L., *The Strengths of Chemical Bonds*, Butterworths, London, 1954.

(68) Skinner, H. A., *Modern Aspects of Thermochemistry*, Royal Institute of Chemistry, London, 1958.

(69) Gunn, S. R., and L. G. Green, *J. Phys. Chem.*, **65**, 779 (1961).

(70) Tannenbaum, S., S. Kaye, and G. F. Lewenz, *J. Am. Chem. Soc.*, **75**, 3753 (1953).

(71) Hobrock, B. G., and R. W. Kiser, *J. Phys. Chem.*, **66**, 155 (1962).

(72) Good, W. D., D. W. Scott, J. L. Lacina, and J. P. McCullough, *J. Phys. Chem.*, **63,** 1139 (1959).
(73) Edstrand, M., *Acta Chem. Scand.*, **9,** 122 (1955).
(74) Sidgwick, N. V., *The Chemical Elements and their Compounds*, Vol. 1, Oxford University Press, London, 1950, p. 287.
(75) Ref. 42, p. 471.
(76) Brewer, L., G. R. Somayajulu, and E. Brackett, *Chem. Rev.*, **63,** 111 (1963).
(77) Orgel, L. E., *J. Chem. Soc.*, **1958**, 4186.

Chapter 6

Compounds of Elements of the First Long Period Whose Highest Oxidation State is Relatively Unstable

I. COMPOUNDS OF ARSENIC, SELENIUM, AND BROMINE

It is well-known (1) that certain elements — notably As, Se, and Br — which follow the transition series in the first long period show a reluctance to form compounds exhibiting the element's highest oxidation state: As^V, Se^{VI}, and Br^{VII}. In some cases, ($AsCl_5$, $HBrO_4$) the compounds are so unstable that they have never been isolated, even though the corresponding compounds of elements in neighboring periods (PCl_5 and $SbCl_5$; $HClO_4$ and HIO_4) are familiar and relatively stable substances. In this section the empirical evidence for the phenomenon is examined.

A. Arsenic

1. Arsenic (V) Halides. The only known pentahalide of arsenic is the fluoride AsF_5, no chloride, bromide, or iodide having yet been isolated. This is in contrast to the behavior of phosphorus, for which only PI_5 is missing from the series of pentahalides, and of antimony, which forms both SbF_5 and $SbCl_5$. The early literature abounds with records of unsuccessful attempts (2, 3, 4, 5, 6) to prepare $AsCl_5$ by the reaction of arsenic trichloride with chlorine under varying conditions of temperature, pressure, and solvent. A claim by Baskerville and Bennett (7) to have isolated $AsCl_5$ as a yellow crystalline solid from the reaction of stoichiometric amounts of $AsCl_3$ and Cl_2 was not substantiated by the

117

phase studies of Smith and Hora (8) and Biltz and Meinecke (9), who showed that the freezing points of $AsCl_3/Cl_2$ mixtures lay on a smooth curve, with no indication of compound formation. Parallel studies (10, 11) of the bromide system $AsBr_3/Br_2$ revealed a similar absence of any pentabromide phase. More recently, Holmes (12) sought evidence for the equilibrium

$$AsX_3 + X_2 \rightleftharpoons AsX_5 \qquad (X = Cl, Br)$$

in solutions of the mixed trihalide and halogen, by measurement of the vapor pressures of the mixtures. No evidence for pentahalide formation was found in the case of the chloride system, although in the case of $X = Br$ a slight negative deviation from ideal behavior was suggestive of $AsBr_5$ formation. In view of the greater ease with which Br^- is oxidized compared to Cl^-, it seems very improbable that $AsBr_5$ would exist if $AsCl_5$ does not. Nevertheless, the possibility that $AsBr_3$ and Br_2 interact in some way in solution is also suggested by the observation (13) that the addition of bromine to ethylenic compounds in acetic acid solution is retarded by the presence of arsenic tribromide in the reaction mixture. It has also been reported (14) that the densities and magnetic susceptibilities of the solutions obtained when solutions of arsenic tribromide and bromine in acetic acid are mixed have values slightly less than those calculated. In view of the fact that the bromine (or iodine) molecule sometimes forms "addition compounds" with donor molecules like dioxane (15), it is conceivable that arsenic tribromide might act as a donor and form a molecular compound of the type

$$Br—Br \ldots AsBr_3$$

in which the dotted line signifies a bond intermediate in character between a van der Waals bond and a covalent bond. Whatever the nature of the interaction, it is quite unlikely that the product is one in which the arsenic atom forms five covalent bonds to separate bromine atoms.

Attempts to stabilize $AsCl_5$ as the anion $AsCl_6^-$ have also failed; for example the addition of KCl or $(CH_3)_4NCl$ to $AsCl_3/Cl_2$ mixtures did not produce a product $M^+AsCl_6^-$. However, the addition of PCl_5 or $SbCl_5$ yielded the compounds $PCl_5 \cdot AsCl_5$ and $SbCl_5 \cdot AsCl_5$, which have been formulated (16) as $AsCl_4^+PCl_6^-$ and $AsCl_4^+SbCl_6^-$, the alternative formulations $PCl_4^+AsCl_6^-$ and $SbCl_4^+AsCl_6^-$ being considered unlikely in the absence of any other evidence for $AsCl_6^-$. The compound of empirical formula AsF_3Cl_2 is also a derivative of the cation $AsCl_4^+$; its formulation $AsCl_4^+AsF_6^-$ is supported (17, 18) by conductance measurements in arsenic trifluoride solution and by the fact that the ion AsF_6^- survives alkaline hydrolysis and can be precipitated as its nitron salt.

Stabilization of $AsCl_5$ with a neutral ligand has been achieved by the use of trimethylphosphine oxide $(CH_3)_3PO$. The complex $AsCl_5 \cdot OP(CH_3)_3$ is formed (19) when chlorine gas is passed into a mixture of arsenic trichloride and trimethylphosphine oxide at 25°C.; the orange crystals which form on cooling decompose slowly on standing in air, or on heating to 50°C.

2. Other Compounds of Arsenic. Although $AsCl_5$ is the most striking example of the instability of As^V, the relative ease of reduction of $AsO_4{}^{3-}$ (arsenate ion) compared to phosphate is another indication of the same phenomenon. The following standard oxidation potentials (E^0, 25°C.) taken from Latimer (20) demonstrate the greater ease with which P^{III} is converted to P^V in aqueous solution.

Acid solution: E^0, volts

$$H_2O + H_3PO_3 \rightarrow H_3PO_4 + 2\,H^+ + 2e \qquad +0.276$$
$$2\,H_2O + HAsO_2 \rightarrow H_3AsO_4 + 2H^+ + 2e \qquad -0.559$$

Basic solution:

$$3\,OH^- + HPO_3{}^{2-} \rightarrow PO_4{}^{3-} + 2\,H_2O + 2e \qquad +1.12$$
$$4\,OH^- + AsO_2{}^- \rightarrow AsO_4{}^{3-} + 2\,H_2O + 2e \qquad +0.67$$

B. Selenium

The most marked example of the relative instability of the highest (VI) oxidation state in selenium is the comparative ease of decomposition of the trioxide SeO_3; its congeners SO_3 and TeO_3 are relatively more stable. Indeed, as recently as 1950, Sidgwick (21) expressed doubts as to the existence of SeO_3. It is not formed from H_2SeO_4 on heating (thermal decomposition of selenic acid yields H_2O, SeO_2, and oxygen), and a report (22) that it is obtained when ozone is passed through a solution of elemental selenium in $SeOCl_2$ was not confirmed (23, 24, 25). The earliest successful procedure for preparing SeO_3 involved the use of a high-frequency glow discharge and dry O_2/Se mixtures; a white sublimate was formed which on solution in sodium hydroxide produced both selenite $(SeO_3{}^{2-})$ and selenate $(SeO_4{}^{2-})$ ions, the latter confirming the presence of the trioxide in the sublimate (26, 27, 28).

More recently, several methods have been devised for obtaining SeO_3 in high yield and in a pure condition — for example, treatment of potassium selenate K_2SeO_4 with sulfur trioxide SO_3(29), and vacuum sublimation of an equimolar mixture of anhydrous selenic acid and phosphorus pentoxide (30).

Selenium trioxide is a white hygroscopic crystalline solid which melts at 118°C.; decomposition into SeO_2 and oxygen begins at about 180°C. and becomes violent at 240–250°C. Its crystal structure has been examined (31) and its heat of formation determined (32).

Although SeO_3 is now a well-established compound, there is no doubt of its instability with respect to decomposition to the lower oxide. It reacts with water to give selenic acid, H_2SeO_4, which decomposes at a lower temperature than does H_2SO_4, and is much more readily reduced in aqueous solution, as the following standard oxidation potentials (20) demonstrate.

Acid solution:

	E^0, volts
$H_2O + H_2SO_3 \rightarrow SO_4{}^{2-} + 4 H^+ + 2e$	-0.17
$H_2O + H_2SeO_3 \rightarrow SeO_4{}^{2-} + 4 H^+ + 2e$	-1.15

Basic solution:

$2 OH^- + SO_3{}^{2-} \rightarrow SO_4{}^{2-} + H_2O + 2e$	$+0.93$
$2 OH^- + SeO_3{}^{2-} \rightarrow SeO_4{}^{2-} + H_2O + 2e$	-0.05

C. Bromine

An oxidation state of $+7$ is evident for the element chlorine in perchloric acid, $HClO_4$, and the perchlorate ion, ClO_4^-. Similar species are well-known in iodine chemistry — periodic acid, HIO_4, and the periodate ion, IO_4^-. In the case of the intermediate element bromine, however, attempts to prepare either perbromic acid, $HBrO_4$, or its salts have so far been unsuccessful. Most of the recorded attempts to prepare perbromic acid were made over half a century ago, and the early literature is described by Mellor (33). Typically, the attempts involved the reaction of bromine with $HClO_4$, Cl_2O_7, or silver perchlorate; Robertson (34) tried to oxidize potassium bromate, $KBrO_3$, with lead dioxide, and bromine with sodium periodate. None of the attempts were successful. Hackspill and Winterer (35) examined the thermal decomposition of anhydrous alkaline earth bromates, but found only bromides among the decomposition products.

D. Theoretical Considerations

The instability of $AsCl_5$, SeO_3, and $HBrO_4$ has usually (36) been considered a consequence of the presence in the first long period of the first transition series of elements. The build-up in nuclear charge which occurs across this series (Sc to Zn), and the comparatively weak screening power of the $3d$ electrons, together have the effect of lowering the energy of the $4s^2$ electron pair in the elements (Ga, Ge, As, Se, Br) which follow the first transition series. Nyholm (37) has expressed the view that in order to achieve the highest or group valence state, the elements from gallium to bromine are required to uncouple the valence-shell $4s^2$ electron pair and promote one of the electrons into a $4p$ (Ga, Ge) or $4d$ (As, Se, Br) orbital. As a result of the tightness with which the $4s^2$ pair is bound in these elements, the $s \rightarrow p$ or $s \rightarrow d$ promotion energy is very large and in unfavorable cases ($AsCl_5$, et cetera) is inadequately offset by the energy recoverable on bond formation. The difficulty of uncoupling the $4s^2$ pair can be demonstrated in various ways. For example in Figure 6.1 the difference (Δ) between (a) the energy required to remove an electron from an s^2p^1 atom or ion (in which the s^2 valence-shell pair remains intact), and (b) that required to remove an electron from an s^2 ion (in which the s^2 pair is uncoupled), is plotted for elements of groups 3, 4, 5, and 6. The quantity Δ is the difference between the fourth and fifth (S, Se, Te), third and fourth (P, As, Sb, Bi), second and third (Si, Ge, Sn, Pb), and first and second (Al, Ga, In, Tl) ionization potentials in electron volts. The high values for Ga, Ge, As, and Se are very striking. Similar high values for Tl, Pb, and Bi are due to a related cause, namely the presence in the third long period of the lanthanide elements; as the $4f$ subshell is progressively occupied, the increasing nuclear charge is only partly offset by the screening power of the added electrons, and the $6s^2$ electron pair in the ensuing elements is very tightly bound.

It is clear, however, that the $s \rightarrow p$ or $s \rightarrow d$ promotion energy *alone* will not determine the stability of the compounds concerned, and the factor of comparable importance is the strength of the bonds formed by the excited atom. It has already been seen for the Al-Ga-In-Tl sequence (Chapter 5, Section II E) and the Si-Ge-Sn-Pb sequence (Chapter 5, Section III E) that in several series of compounds the *covalent bond strength* ($\bar{D}$) decreases down the group in a fairly regular fashion, in spite of the irregular trend in excitation energy:

	Al	Ga	In	Tl
$\bar{D}_{MCl}$ in $MCl_3(g)$, kcal./mole	100	86	78	65
(second I. P) − (first I. P.), e.v.	12.84	14.51	13.07	14.26
$s^2p \rightarrow sp^2$ promotion energy, kcal./mole	83.0	108.5	100.0	129.3

	Si	Ge	Sn	Pb
$\bar{D}_{MCl}$, in $MCl_4(g)$, kcal./mole	94	82	77	58
$\bar{D}_{MH}$ in $MH_4(g)$, kcal./mole	77	69	60	−
$\bar{D}_{MC}$ in $M(CH_3)_4(g)$, kcal./mole	73	61	52	34
(third I. P.) − (second I. P.), e.v.	17.12	18.28	15.86	16.90
$s^2p^2 \rightarrow sp^3$ promotion energy, kcal./mole	95.3	119.9	113.3	145

These figures show that bonds formed by Ga and Ge, while being weaker than those formed by the preceding-row elements Al and Si, are stronger than those of the following-row elements In and Sn.

Apparently in groups 3 and 4 the higher excitation energies required in Ga and Ge (compared to In and Sn) are compensated for by the formation of strong covalent bonds by the excited atoms. In the cases of groups 5, 6, and 7 however, it seems as though the high $s \rightarrow d$ and $p \rightarrow d$ promotion energies required to excite the As, Se, and Br atoms are not adequately offset by high intrinsic bond energies, with the result that $AsCl_5$, SeO_3, and BrO_4^- are unstable. Bond-energy data for the group 5 fluorides MF_5 (M = P, As, Sb, Bi) might reveal this effect, but these unfortunately are not all available. In group 6, however, heats of formation of the gaseous fluorides MF_6 (M = S, Se, Te) have been determined and the mean thermochemical bond energies $\bar{D}_{MF}$ can be evaluated. The required data (38) and the bond energies are as follows.

Heats of formation from elements in their standard states, ΔH_f^0 (25°C.), kcal./mole

$SF_6(g)$	$SeF_6(g)$	$TeF_6(g)$	$S(g)$	$Se(g)$	$Te(g)$	$F(g)$
−289	−246	−315	66.4	49.4	46	18.9

Mean thermochemical bond energies, $\bar{D}_{M-F}$, kcal./mole

S—F	Se—F	Te—F
78	68	79

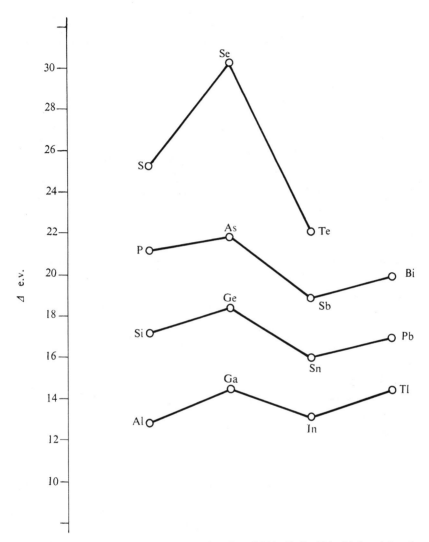

Figure 6.1. Difference (Δ, e.v.) between fourth and fifth (S, Se, Te), third and fourth (P, As, Sb, Bi), second and third (Si, Ge, Sn, Pb), and first and second (Al, Ga, In, Tl) ionization potentials.

In contrast to the regular trends in groups 3 and 4, the Se—F bond in this sequence is weaker than either the S—F or Te—F bonds.

More recently, Urch (39) has examined the decreasing resistance to reduction of the anions XO_4^{n-} along the series $X = Ge$ ($n = 4$), As ($n = 3$), Se ($n = 2$), and Br ($n = 1$), and, like Nyholm, centered attention on the s^2 electron pair of the valence shell. By using rough estimates of the energies of the s and p valence-shell orbitals obtained from atomic spectra, Urch showed that the energy of the $3s$ orbital in Si, P, S, and Cl, and also the energy of the $4s$ orbital in Ge, As, Se, and Br becomes progressively lower from Si to Cl, and from Ge to Br; a result of this trend might be that in Cl and Br the s orbitals differ too much in energy from the $2p$ orbitals of oxygen to bond effectively with them. If this is the case, then in ClO_4^- and BrO_4^- the sigma-bonds to oxygen would be constructed mainly from oxygen $2p$ orbitals and halogen $3p$ (Cl) or $4p$(Br) orbitals rather than halogen sp^3 hybrids. The sigma bonds in XO_4^{n-} anions might therefore decrease in strength from Si to Cl and from Ge to Br; the stability of the anions would then depend increasingly on the efficiency of π-bonding resulting from overlap of the oxygen $2p_\pi$ orbitals with the $3d$ orbitals of Si, P, S, and Cl, or the $4d$ orbitals of Ge, As, Se, and Br. Urch concluded that, because of a difference in radial atomic wave functions, $4d$ orbitals are much less efficient than $3d$ orbitals at π-bonding with $2p_\pi$ orbitals in comparable situations. As a result, ClO_4^- ion is stabilized sufficiently by $3d_\pi - 2p_\pi$ overlap, while in BrO_4^- ion, $4d_\pi - 2p_\pi$ overlap is too inefficient to provide the stabilization necessary to reinforce the sigma bonds.

On this basis it is difficult to account for the renewed stability of the XO_4^{n-} ions (e.g., IO_4^-) which is observed when the second long period is reached, and Urch revived an earlier suggestion due to Hugus (40) that the π-bonding efficiency of the central atom (e.g., Sb, Te, I) is increased by the use of $4f$ rather than $5d$ orbitals.

At present, convincing evidence on this point is lacking although the feasibility of f-orbital hybridization in other circumstances has been accepted (41).

II. COMPOUNDS OF THE ELEMENTS OF THE FIRST TRANSITION SERIES

There is a marked reluctance on the part of many elements of the first transition series (Sc to Zn) to adopt the high oxidation states displayed by their congeners in the second and third transition series. Some outstanding examples are as follows; the compounds in parentheses have not yet been prepared:

(VCl_5)	(CrF_6)	(FeO_4)
$NbCl_5$	MoF_6	RuO_4
$TaCl_5$	WF_6	OsO_4

The absence of VCl_5, CrF_6, and FeO_4 appears to be one aspect of a wide trend that has been mentioned by Sidgwick (42), namely the tendency for high oxidation states to increase in stability (and for low oxidation states to decrease relatively in stability) in passing down a transition-metal group such as V, Nb, Ta or Cr, Mo, W, et cetera. There is abundant evidence to support this generalization (42).

The problem is a very broad one, and in this chapter attention will be confined to a few series of compounds from the Ti, V, and Cr subgroups.

A. Energetic Considerations

Although there is the usual frustrating scarcity of thermodynamic data for groups of transition elements, there is sufficient information available to establish two trends:

(1) The covalent bond strength in compounds of elements in high oxidation states *increases* down each vertical group for which data are available.

(2) The energy difference between high oxidation state and low oxidation state compounds of the same element *widens* as each vertical group is descended, i.e., high oxidation states gain stability at the expense of low ones, as a vertical group is descended.

It is interesting that these trends are just the reverse of those observed in the groups following the transition elements where, as discussed in Chapter 5, the covalent bond strength *decreases* in many cases, and the low oxidation states (Tl^I, Pb^{II}, Bi^{III}) gain stability at the expense of high ones, as a vertical group is descended.

The groups Ti, Zr, Hf; V, Nb, Ta; and Cr, Mo, W will now be discussed in detail.

B. Titanium, Zirconium, Hafnium

The following heat data have been used to evaluate bond energies and to construct the enthalpy diagram (Figure 6.3). Silicon compounds have been included for comparative purposes.

Heats of formation from elements in their standard states, ΔH_f^0 (25°C.), kcal./mole

Si(g)	Ti(g)	Zr(g)	Hf(g)	F(g)	Cl(g)
108[a]	113[b]	146[b]	168[b]	18.9[a]	28.94[a]

SiF_4(g)	TiF_4(s)	ZrF_4(s)	HfF_4(s)	$TiCl_4$(l)	$TiCl_4$(g)	$ZrCl_4$(s)
−372.5[a]	−394.2[c]	−456.8[d]	−461.4[c]	−192.3[a]	−182.4[a]	−233[a]

$HfCl_4$(s)	$TiCl_3$(s)	$ZrCl_3$(s)	$HfCl_3$(s)	$TiCl_2$(s)	$ZrCl_2$(s)	$HfCl_2$(s)
−237[a]	−170.7[f]	−178.6[e]	−195[g]	−123[h]	−124.3[e]	−130[e]

Heats of sublimation, ΔH^0(25°C), kcal./mole

TiF_4	ZrF_4	HfF_4	$ZrCl_4$	$HfCl_4$
22.9[i]	64.3[j]	~60[k]	28.5[j]	24.6[l]

Heats of atomization of gaseous dioxides, ΔH (25°C.), kcal./mole

SiO_2(g)	TiO_2(g)	ZrO_2(g)	HfO_2(g)
300[m]	315[m]	347[m]	360[m]

[a] ref. (38); [b] Table 1.1; [c] ref. (43); [d] ref. (44); [e] ref. (45); [f] ref. (46); [g] ref. (47); [h] ref. (48); [i] ref. (49); [j] ref. (50); [k] assumed; it is not expected to differ much from the value for ZrF_4. [l] ref. (51); [m] ref. (52).

Calculated mean thermochemical bond energies (25°C.), kcal./mole

	M = Si	Ti	Zr	Hf
$\bar{D}_{MO}$ in MO_2(g)	150	158	174	180
$\bar{D}_{MF}$ in MF_4(g)	139	140	154	161
$\bar{D}_{MCl}$ in MCl_4(g)	94	103	117	124

The bond energies, together with the sublimation heats of the elements, are plotted in Figure 6.2. The sublimation heats of Ge, Sn, and Pb and the $\bar{D}_{MCl}$ bond energies (M = Ge, Sn, Pb) are shown for comparative purposes.

It is clear from this figure that the covalent bond strength in the gaseous MX_4 halides increases along the series M = Si, Ti, Zr, Hf, in marked contrast to the decrease observed along the series M = Si, Ge, Sn, Pb. It is interesting that the heats of sublimation of the metals, which reflect the strengths of the metallic bonds in the crystalline elements, show the same trends.

The enthalpies of the tetrachlorides relative to the trichlorides and dichlorides are shown in Figure 6.3. The heat expenditure on atomization of the elements increases from Si to Hf (following the heats of sublimation of Si, Ti, Zr, and Hf), but this is more than recovered by the increasingly exothermic process of forming four covalent M—Cl bonds, so that the heats of formation of the tetrachlorides become more negative in passing from Si to Hf. The heats of formation of the dichlorides MCl_2 are all very similar, so that the enthalpy separation between MCl_4 and $MCl_2 + Cl_2$ is much larger for M = Zr or Hf than for M = Ti.

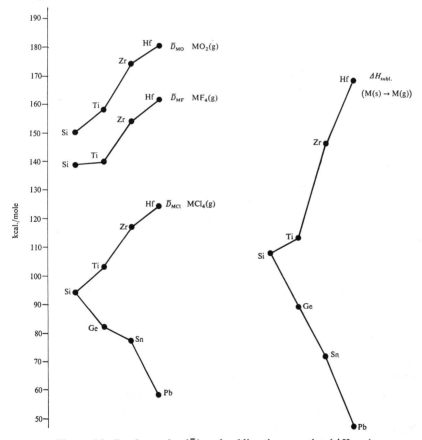

Figure 6.2. Bond energies ($\bar{D}$) and sublimation energies ($\Delta H_{subl.}$).

It is not easy to see why the bond energies increase with rise in atomic weight; as usual the trend may have its origin in variations in either the promotion energies required to excite the metal atoms to suitable valence

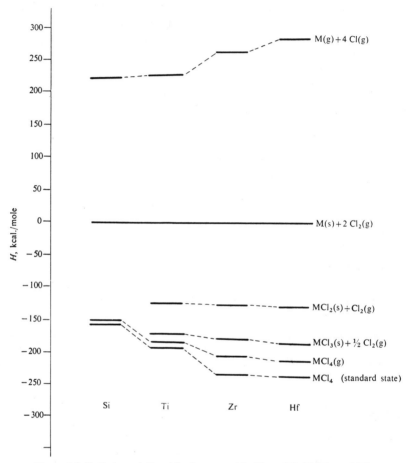

Figure 6.3. Enthalpy relationships between chlorides of Si, Ti, Zr, and Hf.

states, or in the intrinsic bond energies evolved when the excited atoms combine to form the gas-phase molecules.

Pilcher and Skinner (53) have made a study of the valence-states of $TiCl_4$, and concluded that in this molecule a state derived from the configuration d^3s, with tetrahedral (Td) symmetry, is likely to be preferred to one derived from the configuration sp^3, although a hybrid involving both d^3s and sp^3 configurations is more satisfactory than either separately. If the separation between the ground-state (d^2s^2) level and the lowest-lying level of the excited d^3s configuration of the gas-phase atom can be taken as a relative measure of the $d^2s^2 \rightarrow d^3s$ promotion energy, then the values of this separation for Ti, Zr, and Hf, taken from Moore (54) and tabulated below, suggest a slightly more ready promotion in Zr, but a considerably more endothermic process for Hf. This order is certainly not that of the bond energies.

$$d^2s^2 - d^3s \text{ separation}$$

	cm^{-1}	e.v.	kcal./mole
Ti	6557	0.81	18.8
Zr	4871	0.60	13.9
Hf	14092	1.74	40.3

The resistance to promotion of the hafnium $6s$ electron seems to be a consequence of the relatively ineffective screening provided by the inner $4f$ electrons. In the absence of further knowledge as to the orbitals used by Ti, Zr, and Hf in the MX_4 molecules, and of the relevant excitation energies and bond strengths, it is difficult to account for the increasing values of $\bar{D}_{MX}$ from Ti to Hf.

An ionic-model enthalpy cycle (cf. Chapter 5, Section II E) is rather more informative, and is illustrated for the dioxides $MO_2(M = Ti, Zr, Hf)$ using the following data.

Heats of formation from elements in their standard states, ΔH_f^0 (25°C.), kcal./mole

$TiO_2(s)$	$ZrO_2(s)$	$HfO_2(s)$	$O(g)$	$O^{2-}(g)$
-225.8^a	-261.5^a	-266.1^a	59.55^b	217^c

Ionization Potentials, e.v. (from Table 6.1).

	Ti	Zr	Hf
First	6.82	6.98	7.9
Second	13.57	13.13	14.9
First + second	20.39	20.11	22.8
Third	27.47	22.98	23.3
Fourth	43.24	34.33	33.3
Total for four electrons	91.10	77.42	79.4

Calculated lattice enthalpies, 25°C., kcal./mole

TiO$_2$	ZrO$_2$	HfO$_2$
2879	2632	2705

[a] ref. (38); [b] Table 1.3; [c] ref. (69).

The lattice enthalpies may be correlated with the sizes of the M^{4+} ions, as listed by Pauling (71):

	Ti^{4+}	Zr^{4+}	Hf^{4+}
ionic radius (Å)	0.68	0.80	0.81

The lattice enthalpy decreases from TiO$_2$ to ZrO$_2$ as the M^{4+} radius (and hence the internuclear distance in the crystal) increases; ZrO$_2$ and HfO$_2$ have lattice enthalpies which differ by less than three percent, in accord with the similar radii of the Zr^{4+} and Hf^{4+} ions.

The enthalpy data are summarized in Figure 6.3a, from which it can be seen that the heat required to atomize the elements from their standard states increases from Ti to Hf, since the heat of sublimation of the metal increases in this order. Formation of the gaseous ions M^{4+}(g) and 2 O^{2-}(g) then depends on the (constant) electron affinity of the oxygen atom, and the ionization potentials (for four electrons) of the metal atom. The ionization enthalpy decreases sharply (by about 13.7 e.v., or 315 kcal./mole) between Ti and Zr, and rises slightly (by 2 e.v.) between Zr and Hf. The smaller ionization potential of Zr more than compensates for the decrease in lattice enthalpy (247 kcal./mole) between TiO$_2$ and ZrO$_2$, and also offsets the fact that the heat of sublimation of Zr metal is about 33 kcal./mole higher than that of Ti; the balance of these effects is that ZrO$_2$ is formed from its elements more exothermically than TiO$_2$. The heat of formation of HfO$_2$ is very similar to that of ZrO$_2$, since the rather higher heats of ionization and sublimation of Hf are balanced by a slightly bigger lattice enthalpy in HfO$_2$.

Heats of formation of the low-valence monoxides MO are unfortunately not known for all three elements, but it would be surprising if these show the same pronounced trend between TiO and ZrO as do the dioxides MO$_2$; this is suggested by the fact that although the ionization potentials for *four* electrons drop sharply from Ti (91.10 e.v.) to Zr (77.42 e.v.), the ionization potentials for *two* electrons are almost the same for Ti (20.39 e.v.) and Zr (20.11 e.v.). This means that while the formation of gaseous M^{4+}(g) ions occurs much more readily for Zr than for Ti,

$$Ti(s) - 4e \rightarrow Ti^{4+}(g) \qquad \varDelta H = +2219 \text{ kcal./mole}$$
$$Zr(s) - 4e \rightarrow Zr^{4+}(g) \qquad \varDelta H = +1936 \text{ kcal./mole}$$

the ease of formation of the gaseous *dipositive* ions M^{2+} is in the reverse order:

$$Ti(s) - 2e \rightarrow Ti^{2+}(g) \qquad \varDelta H = +586 \text{ kcal./mole}$$
$$Zr(s) - 2e \rightarrow Zr^{2+}(g) \qquad \varDelta H = +610 \text{ kcal./mole}$$

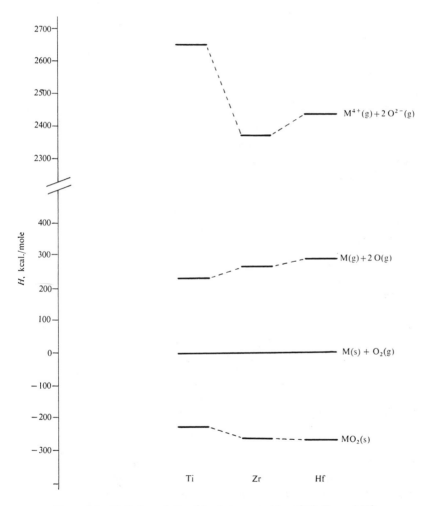

Figure 6.3a. Enthalpy relationships between oxides of Ti, Zr, and Hf.

Thus, zirconium is more able to overcome the energetic disadvantage of a lower lattice energy by forming Zr^{IV} rather than Zr^{II} compounds. In this connection it is significant that the heats of formation of $TiCl_2(s)$ (-123 kcal./mole) and $ZrCl_2(s)$ (-124 kcal./mole) are almost the same. Ionization potential data are incomplete for the transition elements (especially the third series), but the values shown in Table 6.1 point to

Table 6.1
Ionization Potentials, e.v.

	Ti	Zr	Hf	V	Nb	Ta
First	6.82	6.98	7.9[a]	6.74	6.88	7.88
Second	13.57	13.13	14.9	14.65	14.32	16.2
First+second	20.39	20.11	22.8	21.39	21.20	24.08
Third	27.47	22.98	23.3[b]	29.31	25.04	
Fourth	43.24	34.33	33.3[b]	48	38.3	
Fifth				65.2	50	

	Cr	Mo	W	Mn	Tc	Re
First	6.76	7.10	7.98	7.43	7.28	7.87
Second	16.49	16.15	17.7	15.64	15.26	16.6[d]
First+second	23.25	23.25	25.68	23.07	22.54	24.47
Third	30.95	27.13		33.69	29.54[c]	
Fourth	49.6	46.4				
Fifth	73	61.2				
Sixth	90.6	68				

Data are from Moore (54), except: [a] estimated by comparison with values for Ta, W, and Re; [b] ref. (70); [c] ref. (72); [d] ref. (73).

an apparently general feature: in passing from the first transition series (Ti, V, Cr, Mn) to the second (Zr, Nb, Mo, Tc), there is little change in the sum of the first two ionization potentials, whereas a substantial drop occurs in the third and fourth ionization potentials. The trend in passing from the second transition series to the third is for the sum of the first two ionization potentials to increase; the third and fourth ionization potentials, at least in hafnium, seem to remain substantially unaltered. In general, it would therefore seem energetically more profitable for the elements of the second and third transition series to form cations with high rather than low charges, that is, to form compounds showing high rather than low oxidation states. This is certainly the empirical trend.

Pilcher and Skinner have noted (53) that the mean thermochemical bond energy $\bar{D}_{MCl}$ *increases* along the series of gaseous molecules $TiCl_4$, $TiCl_3$, and $TiCl_2$:

	$TiCl_4(g)$	$TiCl_3(g)$	$TiCl_2(g)$
$\bar{D}_{MCl}$, kcal./mole	103	109	120

The corresponding data for the lower chlorides of zirconium and hafnium might shed some light on the problem, but the necessary heats of atomization are not known.

C. Vanadium, Niobium, Tantalum

Again in this group, bond energies have been evaluated and enthalpy diagrams constructed from the following data.

Heats of formation from elements in their standard states, ΔH_f^0 (25°C.), kcal./mole

$NbCl_5(s)$	$NbCl_5(g)$	$TaCl_5(s)$	$TaCl_5(g)$	$VCl_4(l)$	$VCl_4(g)$
-190.5[a]	-169.9[a]	-205.0[b]	-182.7[b]	-136.2[c]	-126.7[d]

$NbCl_4(s)$	$NbCl_4(g)$	$TaCl_4(s)$	$TaCl_4(g)$	$VCl_3(s)$	$NbCl_3(s)$
-166.0[a]	-136.6[a]	-168.8[b]	-136.3[b]	-143[k]	-139[a]

$TaCl_3(s)$	$VCl_2(s)$	$NbCl_2(s)$	$V(g)$	$Nb(g)$	$Ta(g)$
-130.5[b]	-110[e]	-98[a]	123[f]	185[f]	186.8[f]

$VF_5(l)$		$NbF_5(s)$		
-352[h] ($\Delta H_{vap.} = 10.6$[i])		-432[j] ($\Delta H_{subl.} = 23$[c])		

Heats of atomization of gaseous dioxides, ΔH (25°C.), kcal./mole

$VO_2(g)$	$NbO_2(g)$	$TaO_2(g)$
298[g]	320[g]	351[g]

[a] ref. (55); [b] ref. (56); [c] ref. (65); [d] calculated from data for the liquid together with its heat of vaporization (50) = 9.5 kcal./mole; [e] ref. (48); [f] Table 1.1; [g] ref. (52); [h] ref. (57); [i] ref. (58); [j] ref. (59); [k] ref. (60).

Calculated mean thermochemical bond energies (25°C.), kcal./mole

M=	V	Nb	Ta
$\bar{D}_{MO}$ in $MO_2(g)$	149	160	176
$\bar{D}_{MCl}$ in $MCl_4(g)$	91	109	110
$\bar{D}_{MCl}$ in $MCl_5(g)$	–	100	103
$\bar{D}_{MF}$ in $MF_5(g)$	112	134	–

These bond energies, for both M^{IV} and M^V compounds, increase from V to Ta, as do the heats of sublimation of the metals. The trends are similar to those shown by Ti, Zr, and Hf.

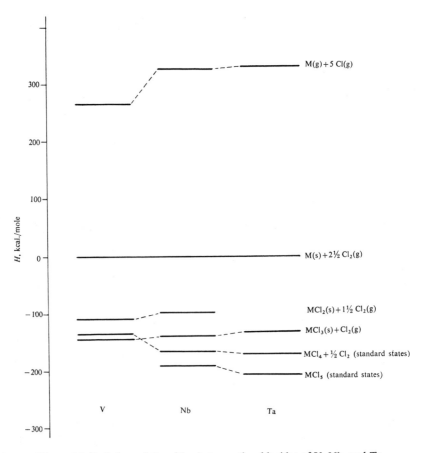

Figure 6.4. Enthalpy relationships between the chlorides of V, Nb, and Ta.

The enthalpy data for the chlorides in the various oxidation states are shown in Figure 6.4. The "missing" compound is vanadium (V) chloride, VCl_5. Pilcher and Skinner (53) consider that a molecule such as VCl_5 would be derived from a d^3sp configuration of the vanadium atom, with perhaps ten percent admixture of dsp^3. Their calculations show that the formation of VCl_5 from the stable VCl_4 would involve an extra excitation energy of about 3 e.v., and that this factor, combined with the increased steric repulsion associated with the trigonal bipyramid structure, may be responsible for the instability of VCl_5.

D. Chromium, Molybdenum, Tungsten

Bond energies have been calculated and enthalpy diagrams constructed from the following data; sulfur compounds have been included for comparison.

Heats of Formation from elements in their standard states, ΔH_f^0 (25°C.), kcal./mole

$SO_3(s)$	$SO_3(g)$	$CrO_3(s)$	$MoO_3(s)$	$WO_3(s)$		
-110.1^a	-94.4^b	-138.5^b	-178.2^b	-201.5^b		
$SO_2(g)$	$CrO_2(s)$	$MoO_2(s)$	$WO_2(s)$	$SF_6(g)$	$MoF_6(g)$	$WF_6(g)$
-70.95^b	-141^a	-139.5^b	-140.9^e	-289^h	-382^h	-416^h
$S(g)$	$Cr(g)$	$Mo(g)$	$W(g)$	$O(g)$	$F(g)$	
66.4^c	95^d	157.5^d	200^d	59.55^c	18.9^c	

Heats of sublimation, ΔH (25°C.), kcal./mole

CrO_3	MoO_3	WO_3
$\sim 28^f$	102^g	127^g

[a] ref. (61); [b] ref. (50); [c] Table 1.3; [d] Table 1.1; [e] ref. (62); [f] ref. (63); [g] ref. (64); [h] ref. (38).

Calculated mean thermochemical bond energies (25°C.), kcal./mole

M =	S	Cr	Mo	W
$\bar{D}_{MO}$ in $MO_3(g)$	113	128	138	151
$\bar{D}_{MF}$ in $MF_6(g)$	78	—	109	122

The bond energies show the same general increase from Cr to W as was noted in the series Ti, Zr, Hf and V, Nb, Ta.

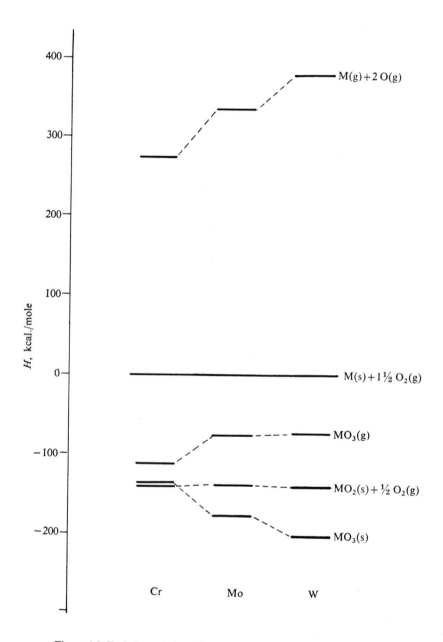

Figure 6.5. Enthalpy relationships between oxides of Cr, Mo, and W.

The enthalpy data for the oxides are shown in Figure 6.5. The energy expended on atomization of the elements rises from Cr to W, following the rise in heat of sublimation of the metal. The energy recovered on

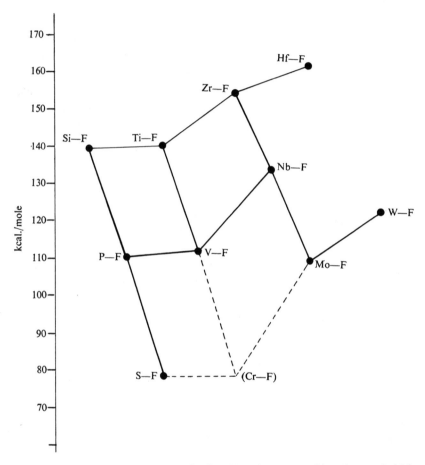

Figure 6.6. Trends in bond energies for fluorides of some transition elements in high oxidation states.

bond formation rises from Cr to W, but of the *gaseous* trioxides, CrO_3 has the most negative heat of formation. It is the much larger heats of sublimation of MoO_3 and WO_3 which give these two *solid* oxides the most negative heats of formation. The difference in enthalpy between the dioxides and the trioxides in their standard states widens from Cr to W, i.e., the trioxides become more stable from Cr to W with respect to decomposition into the lower oxide and oxygen.

In the fluoride sequence, CrF_6 has never been isolated. The mean bond energy in $CrF_6(g)$ can be guessed roughly by extrapolation procedures; the values of $\bar{D}_{MF}$ in SiF_4 (139) and TiF_4(140), and also in PF_5(110) and VF_5(112) are almost the same for each pair, which suggests that $\bar{D}_{MF}$ in SF_6(78) and CrF_6 may not differ much. The collected M—F bond energy data shown in Figure 6.6 support the choice of 78 kcal./mole for $\bar{D}_{MF}$ in $CrF_6(g)$ as not unreasonable. (The data for Figure 6.6 have already been presented in this chapter, except $\bar{D}_{MF}$ in $PF_5(g)$ — 110 kcal./mole — which was calculated from the heats of formation of $PF_5(g)$ = -381.4 kcal./mole (66) and $P(g)$ = 75 kcal./mole (50)).

Using the value 78 kcal./mole for the Cr—F bond energy, ΔH_f^0 for $CrF_6(g)$ can be estimated to be ~ -260 kcal./mole. Now the highest fluoride of chromium for which a heat of formation is known is the tetrafluoride CrF_4, although CrF_5 has been reported (67). ΔH_f^0 for $CrF_4(s)$ = -286.5 kcal./mole (50). Hence the reaction

$$CrF_4(s) + F_2(g) \rightarrow CrF_6(g)$$

is likely to be endothermic by about 26.5 kcal./mole. The endothermicity could be reduced by the condensation of $CrF_6(g)$ to a liquid or solid, but this would be partly offset by the fact that the entropy change would thereby become less favorable. Thus the apparent nonexistence of CrF_6 seems to be supported by thermodynamic considerations, although the possibility of its formation in a small equilibrium proportion, or under conditions other than the standard ones to which the thermodynamic quantities refer, cannot be excluded.

The two extra Cr—F bonds in CrF_6 must be very weak indeed; if the heat of sublimation of CrF_4 is about the same as that of TiF_4 (both solids sublime in a vacuum over similar temperature ranges), namely 22.9 kcal./mole, then ΔH_f^0 for $CrF_4(g)$ is about -263 kcal./mole, which is within a few kcal. of the estimated heat of formation of $CrF_6(g)$. The enthalpy change for the conversion of $CrF_4(g)$ to $CrF_6(g)$ is therefore close to zero, i.e., the fission of the covalent bond in the F_2 molecule (~ 38 kcal./mole) is just balanced by the formation of the two new Cr—F bonds, whose energies therefore average only about 19 kcal./mole. This very low value must be due to either an excessively high promotion energy, or a very low intrinsic bond strength, or both; the problem of the bearing of excitation and bond energies on the instability of CrF_6 has been discussed inconclusively by Skinner and Sumner (68).

REFERENCES

(1) Sidgwick, N.V., *The Chemical Elements and their Compounds*, Vol. 1, Oxford University Press, London, 1950, p. 815.

(2) Rose, H., *Poggendorf's Ann.*, **52,** 62 (1841).

(3) Mayrhofer, J., *Ann.*, **158,** 326 (1871).

(4) Janowsky, J. V., *Z. Anorg. Chem.*, **6,** 219 (1873).

(5) Sloan, B. E., *Chem. News*, **44,** 203 (1881).

(6) Besson, A., *Compt. rend.*, **109,** 940 (1889).

(7) Baskerville, C., and H. H. Bennett, *J. Am. Chem. Soc.*, **24,** 1070 (1902).

(8) Smith, W. R., and J. E. Hora, *J. Am. Chem. Soc.*, **265,** 632 (1904).

(9) Biltz, W., and E. Meinecke, *Z. Anorg. Allgem. Chem.*, **131,** 1 (1923).

(10) Biltz, W., and K. Jeep, *Z. Anorg. Allgem. Chem.*, **162,** 32 (1927).

(11) Pushin, N. A., and J. Makuc, *Z. Anorg. Allgem. Chem.*, **237,** 177 (1938).

(12) Holmes, R. R., *J. Inorg. Nucl. Chem.*, **19,** 363 (1961).

(13) Venkataraman, R., *Proc. Indian Acad. Sci.*, **13A,** 259 (1941).

(14) Savithri, K., *Proc. Indian Acad. Sci.*, **16A,** 196 (1942).

(15) Hassel, O., and C. Rømming, *Quart. Rev. (London)*, **16,** 1 (1962).

(16) Gutmann, V., *Monatsh.*, **82,** 473 (1951); *Z. Anorg. Allgem. Chem.*, **264,** 151 (1951).

(17) Kolditz, L., *Z. Anorg. Allgem. Chem.*, **280,** 313 (1955).

(18) Dess, H. M., R. W. Parry, and G. L. Vidale, *J. Am. Chem. Soc.*, **78,** 5730 (1956).

(19) Lindqvist, I., and G. Olofsson, *Acta Chem. Scand.*, **13,** 1753 (1959)

(20) Latimer, W. M., *Oxidation Potentials*, 2nd ed., Prentice-Hall, Inc., New York, 1952.

(21) Sidgwick, N.V., ref. (1) p. 971.

(22) Worsley, R. R. le G., and H. H. Baker, *J. Chem. Soc.*, **123,** 2870 (1923).

(23) Meyer, J., and A. Pawletta, *Ber.*, **60,** 985 (1927).

(24) Hoffmann, G. F., and V. Lenher, *J. Am. Chem. Soc.*, **51,** 3177 (1929).

(25) Smith, G. B. L., and C. L. Mehltretter, *J. Am. Chem. Soc.*, **53,** 3562 (1931).

(26) Rheinboldt, H., A. Hessel, and K. Schwenzer, *Ber.*, **63,** 1865 (1930).

(27) Kramer, E. N., and V. W. Meloche, *J. Am. Chem. Soc.*, **56,** 1081 (1934).

(28) Olsen, E., and V. W. Meloche, *J. Am. Chem. Soc.*, **58,** 2511, 2514 (1936).

(29) Lehmann, H. A., and G. Kruger, *Naturwissenschaften*, **38,** 208 (1951); *Z. Anorg. Allgem. Chem.*, **267,** 324 (1952).

(30) Toul, F., and K. Dostal, *Chem. Listy*, **36,** 132 (1952).

(31) Mijlhoff, F. C., and C. H. McGillivray, *Acta Cryst.*, **15**, 620 (1962).
(32) Mijlhoff, F. C., *Rec. Trav. Chim.*, **82**, 822 (1963).
(33) Mellor, J. W., *A Comprehensive Treatise on Inorganic and Theoretical Chemistry*, Vol. 2, Longmans, Green and Co., London, 1946.
(34) Robertson, P. W., *Chem. News*, **106**, 50 (1912).
(35) Hackspill, L., and Winterer, *Compt. rend.*, **191**, 663 (1930).
(36) Lakatos, B., *Acta Chim. Acad. Sci. Hung.*, **8**, 219 (1955).
(37) Nyholm, R. S., *Proc. Chem. Soc.*, 273 (1961).
(38) Lewis, G. N., and M. Randall, *Thermodynamics*, revised by K. S. Pitzer and L. Brewer, 2nd ed., McGraw-Hill, New York, 1961.
(39) Urch, D. S., *J. Inorg. Nucl. Chem.*, **25**, 771 (1963).
(40) Hugus, Z Z., *J. Am. Chem. Soc.*, **74**, 1076 (1952).
(41) Coulson, C. A., and G. R. Lester, *J. Chem. Soc.*, **1956**, 3650.
(42) Sidgwick, N. V., ref. (1), for example pp. 628, 804, 998.
(43) Greenberg, E., J. L. Settle, and W. N. Hubbard, *J. Phys. Chem.*, **66**, 1345 (1962).
(44) Greenberg, E., J. L. Settle, H. M. Feder, and W. N. Hubbard, *J. Phys. Chem.*, **65**, 1168 (1961).
(45) Lungu, S. N., *Acad. Rep. Populare Romine, Studii Cercetari Fiz.*, **13**, No. 1, 29 (1962), through *Chem. Abstr.* **57**, 9297 (1962).
(46) Altman, D., M. Farber, and D. M. Mason, *J. Chem. Phys.*, **25**, 531 (1956).
(47) Ruzinov, L. P., and S. F. Belov, *Tsvetn. Metal.*, **35**, No. 9, 85 (1962); through *Chem. Abstr.*, **58**, 6528 (1963).
(48) Brewer, L., G. R. Somayajulu, and E. Brackett, *Chem. Rev.*, **63**, 111 (1963).
(49) Hall, E. H., J. M. Blocher Jr., and I. E. Campbell, *J. Electrochem. Soc.* **105**, 275 (1958).
(50) Kubaschewski, O., and E. L. Evans, *Metallurgical Thermochemistry*, Pergamon Press, Ltd., London, 1956.
(51) Chu, S. Y., and I. S. Morozov, *Zh. Neorgan. Khim.*, **4**, 492 (1959), through *Chem. Abstr.*, **53**, 15681 (1959).
(52) Brewer, L., and G. M. Rosenblatt, *Chem. Rev.*, **61**, 257 (1961).
(53) Pilcher, G., and H. A. Skinner, *J. Inorg. Nucl. Chem.*, **7**, 8 (1958).
(54) Moore, C. E., *Atomic Energy Levels, Nat. Bur. Std. (U.S.), Circ.* **467**, Vol. 1 (1949), Vol. 2 (1952), Vol. 3 (1958).
(55) Schafer, H., and F. Kahlenburg, *Z. Anorg. Allgem. Chem.*, **305**, 291 (1960).
(56) Schafer, H., and F. Kahlenburg, *Z. Anorg. Allgem. Chem.*, **305**, 178 (1960).
(57) Cavell, R. C., and H. C. Clark, *Trans. Faraday Soc.*, **59**, 2706 (1963).
(58) Clark, H. C., *Chem. Rev.*, **58**, 869 (1958).
(59) Myers, O. E., and A. P. Brady, *J. Phys. Chem.* **64**, 591 (1960).
(60) Shchukarev, S. A., I. V. Vasilkova, I. L. Perfilova, and L. V. Chernykh, *Zh. Neorgan. Khim.*, **7**, 1509 (1962), through *Chem. Abstr.* **57**, 15897 (1962).
(61) Brewer, L., *Chem. Rev.*, **52**, 1 (1953).
(62) Mah, A. D., *J. Am. Chem. Soc.*, **81**, 1582 (1959).
(63) Ariya, S. M., S. A. Shchukarev, and V. B. Glushkova, *Zh. Obshch. Khim.*, **23**, 2063 (1953), through *Chem. Abstr.*, **48**, 13396 (1954).

(64) Glemser, O., and R. J. Haeseler, *Z. Anorg. Allgem. Chem.*, **316,**168 (1962).

(65) Gross, P., and C. Hayman, *Trans. Faraday Soc.*, **60,** 45 (1964).

(66) Gross, P., Hayman, C., Levy, D. L., and Stuart, M. C., quoted by G. T. Armstrong and L. A. Krieger, in J. F. Masi and D. H. Tsai, eds., *Progress in International Research on Thermodynamic and Transport Properties*, Academic Press Inc., New York, 1962, p. 8.

(67) von Wartenberg, H., *Z. Anorg. Allgem. Chem.*, **247,** 135 (1941).

(68) Skinner, H. A., and F. H. Sumner, *J. Inorg. Nucl. Chem.*, **4,** 245 (1957).

(69) Waddington, T. C., in H. J. Emeleus and A. G. Sharpe, eds., *Advances in Inorganic Chemistry and Radiochemistry*, Vol. 1, Academic Press, Inc., New York, 1959, p. 157.

(70) Klinkenberg, P. F. A., T. A. M. Van Kleef, and P. E. Noorman, *Physica*, **27,** 1177 (1961).

(71) Pauling, L., *The Nature of the Chemical Bond*, 3rd ed., Cornell University Press, New York, 1960.

(72) Catalan, M. A., and F. R. Rico, *Chem. Abstr.*, **54,** 2929 (1960).

(73) Meggers, W. F., M. A. Catalan, and M. Sales, *J. Res. Nat. Bur. Std.*, **61,** 441 (1958).

Chapter 7

Some Compounds of the Noble Gases

I. GENERAL

This book is concerned with compounds which, although conforming to the simpler requirements of valence theory, are either nonexistent or highly unstable under ordinary conditions. Before 1962, compounds of the noble gases would not have warranted discussion: such compounds (with the exception of ephemeral gas-phase species and some clathrates) had certainly never been prepared, but for what at that time was considered to be an obvious reason — their very nonexistence had itself become established as an almost sacrosanct rule of valence. Predictions of their likely existence, like that of Pimentel (1), were largely ignored. In 1962, however, there appeared a report of the preparation by Bartlett (2) of a compound of xenon ($XePtF_6$) which was a stable solid at room temperature, and this was followed in the ensuing two years by the publication of over sixty papers describing the preparation and properties of a moderate range of noble-gas compounds. The existence of such compounds has, in a remarkably short time, become an accepted fact of chemistry, and it is therefore pertinent to inquire why the range of noble-gas compounds is not more extensive than it in fact is at present. The literature on these compounds is expanding rapidly, but the present (1964) position is that compounds of *xenon* are by far the best known and most accessible; the few compounds of krypton are relatively unstable, and investigation of the corresponding compounds of radon has of course been hampered by that element's scarcity and radioactivity. Compounds of helium, neon, and argon have yet to be prepared. The xenon compounds comprise for the most part a group of fluorides (but no other halides); a group of oxides (but no other chalcogenides); and a small number of saltlike compounds which, like $XePtF_6$, apparently contain the unipositive cation Xe^+.

This chapter will be limited to a discussion of the halides and the Xe^+ compounds.

II. CHLORIDES, BROMIDES, AND IODIDES
OF THE NOBLE GASES

The established halides of the noble gases comprise a relatively small group of fluorides of krypton, xenon, and radon; of these, XeF_4 and XeF_2 were among the first noble-gas compounds discovered (3, 4). No chloride, bromide, or iodide of any of the noble gases has yet been isolated and characterized, nor has any halide of helium, neon, or argon. A search for the factors responsible for the limited nature of this array of noble-gas halides leads inevitably to a consideration of the character of the bonding in the compounds, and a summary of the various theoretical approaches which have been made to this problem has been given by Coulson (5). Of these approaches, the molecular orbital and the valence bond (resonance) methods provide a theoretical basis for three empirically-observed characteristics of noble-gas halide formation. These three characteristics are that noble gas halide formation occurs most readily if

(a) the noble gas atom has a low ionization potential;
(b) the halogen is small and electronegative; and
(c) the number of ligand halogen atoms is even.

Thus the readiness of noble gas halide formation falls off along the series $Rn > Xe > Kr > Ar > Ne > He$ and $F > Cl > Br > I$.

These points emerge most clearly from a simplified valence bond treatment of XeF_2, xenon difluoride. Since contributions from forms involving the participation of xenon-atom $5d$ orbitals are considered (5) to be energetically improbable, the XeF_2 molecule can be described as a resonance hybrid of essentially two canonical forms

$$F—Xe^+F^- \text{ and } F^-\ ^+Xe—F$$

As Coulson (5) has shown, these forms themselves are relatively stable with respect to their constituent atoms, as is evident from the following reaction sequence based on the formation of the $F—Xe^+ F^-$ model:

$$(1)\ Xe - e \rightarrow Xe^+$$
$$(2)\ F + e \rightarrow F^-$$
$$(3)\ Xe^+ + F^- \rightarrow [Xe^+ F^-]$$
$$(4)\ [Xe^+ F^-] + F \rightarrow F—Xe^+ F^-$$

$$\overline{Xe + 2F \rightarrow F—Xe^+ F^-}$$

If the energy terms are regarded as enthalpy changes at 25°C., then step (1) is the first ionization potential of xenon, $\Delta H = 281.2$ kcal./mole, and step (2) is the electron affinity of fluorine, $\Delta H = -83.5$ kcal./mole. Step (3) is the enthalpy change on bringing the isolated ions Xe^+ and F^- together to the distance observed (7) in XeF_2 from neutron diffraction experiments, 2.00 Å. The energy liberated is approximately $-e^2/r$, which with $r = 2.00 \times 10^{-8}$ cm. gives $\Delta H = -166.0$ kcal./mole. The sum of terms (1), (2), and (3) is thus $281.2 - 83.5 - 166.0 = $ a heat absorption of 31.7 kcal./mole. It is likely that this amount of energy would be recovered in step (4), which is the exothermic formation of the cotvalent Xe—F bond, so that ΔH for the reaction $2 F + Xe \rightarrow F—Xe^+ F^-$ should not differ much from zero, and could even be somewhat negative. Since additional stability accrues from the resonance between the two contributing forms, the stability of XeF_2 is not difficult to understand.

If however *chlorine* Cl is substituted for fluorine in the above reaction sequence, step (1) is of course unaffected, and step (2) is $\Delta H = -87.3$ kcal./mole, which differs only slightly from the value for fluorine. In step (3) however, the larger Cl^- ion will expand the internuclear distance r and thus make the coulomb attractive energy $-e^2/r$ numerically smaller. The extent of the expansion is not known with certainty, but since the I—F bonds in IF_5 and IF_7 (~ 1.8 Å) are shorter than the I—Cl bonds in ICl, ICl_2^-, and ICl_4^- (~ 2.3 Å) (8) by about 0.5 Å, and since the Pauling (6) ionic radii for F^- (1.36 Å) and Cl^- (1.81 Å) differ by roughly the same amount, a reasonable figure for the Xe—Cl distance in hypothetical $XeCl_2$ would be ~ 2.5 Å. On this assumption, the energy of step (3) would be $\Delta H = -132.8$ kcal./mole. The sum of terms (1), (2), and (3) for the chlorine structure is thus $281.2 - 87.3 - 132.8 = 61.1$ kcal./mole, and this is about 30 kcal./mole more positive than the corresponding sum for the fluorine structure. This means that, for $Cl — Xe^+ Cl^-$ and $F—Xe^+ F^-$

to have comparable stabilities, the energy liberated in step (4) must be about 30 kcal./mole greater in the case of the chlorine structure. Since covalent bonds to chlorine are almost invariably weaker (i.e., formed less exothermically) than those to fluorine (see Table 1.9) it is unlikely that this would be the case; indeed the stability of the chlorine structure relative to the fluorine structure would diminish still further on the inclusion of step (4).

It is thus evident that the smaller and the more electronegative is the halogen atom, the more likely it is to form a noble gas halide because steps (3) and (4) become more exothermic with decreasing halogen size. The effect of step (2) is about the same for all four halogens, and is least exothermic for iodine (see Chapter 1, Section II A 1):

$$\Delta H(25°\text{C.}), \text{ kcal./mole, for } \text{hal(g)} + e \rightarrow \text{hal}^-(g)$$

hal = F	83.5
Cl	87.3
Br	82.0
I	75.7

The significance of the ionization potential of the noble gas is also apparent, as the bigger the noble gas, the smaller the ionization potential and hence the smaller the energy absorbed in step (1):

Ionization enthalpies, $\Delta H(25°\text{C.})$, kcal./mole

He	568.2
Ne	498.5
Ar	364.7
Kr	324.1
Xe	281.2
Rn	249.2

The advantage of a low ionization energy would be offset to some extent by a decrease in the energy liberated in step (3) because of the larger size of the noble gas causing a bigger internuclear distance and numerically smaller e^2/r term.

If the above reasoning is correct, a suggestion by Pimentel and Spratley (9) that HeF_2 should exist (it is iso-electronic with HF_2^-) seems unlikely to be sustained, unless the effect of the very high ionization potential of He (step 1) can be outweighed by the formation of sufficiently strong bonds by the small He atom (steps (3) and (4)).

A more empirical approach to the likelihood of the existence of chlorides of the noble gases is as follows: The heat of formation of xenon difluoride $XeF_2(g)$ from its elements in their standard states is about -37 kcal./mole (10). In the reaction sequence

$$F_2(g) \rightarrow 2 F(g) \qquad\qquad \Delta h_1$$
$$Xe(g) + 2 F(g) \rightarrow XeF_2(g) \qquad \Delta h_2$$
$$\overline{Xe(g) + F_2(g) \rightarrow XeF_2(g) \qquad \Delta H_f^0, \ XeF_2(g)}$$

$\Delta h_1 = 37.8$ kcal./mole F_2 (Table 1.3), and $\Delta H_f^0 = -37$ kcal./mole, so that $\Delta h_2 = -74.8$ kcal., and the mean thermochemical bond energy $\bar{D}_{Xe-F}$ in XeF_2 is therefore close to 37 kcal./mole.

If $XeCl_2$ is now considered, then $\Delta h_1 = 57.9$ kcal./mole Cl_2 (Table 1.3), so that in order to make ΔH_f^0 just negative, Δh_2 must be > 58 kcal., i.e., $\bar{D}_{Xe-Cl}$, must be at least 29 kcal./mole. It seems likely that an Xe—Cl bond would be rather weaker than this; bonds formed by chlorine with elements of electronegativity comparable with that of xenon often have energies which are about two-thirds of those of the corresponding bonds formed by fluorine. The electronegativity of xenon, estimated by Mulliken's method (11) with the assumption that the electron affinity of xenon is negligible, is 2.24. Elements with similar electronegativities on Pauling's scale (Table 1.10) are phosphorus (2.1), arsenic (2.0), and carbon (2.5). The mean thermochemical bond energies (kcal./mole) for compounds of these elements with F and Cl are as follows. The bond energies have been calculated from enthalpy data listed by Lewis and Randall (12):

$\bar{D}_{P-F}(PF_3) = 117$	$\bar{D}_{As-F}(AsF_3) = 111$	$\bar{D}_{C-F}(CF_4) = 116$
$\bar{D}_{P-Cl}(PCl_3) = 76$	$\bar{D}_{As-Cl}(AsCl_3) = 69$	$\bar{D}_{C-Cl}(CCl_4) = 78$
ratio $\dfrac{\bar{D}_{X-Cl}}{\bar{D}_{X-F}}$ 0.65	0.62	0.67

If the same relative bond strengths are preserved in the xenon halides, then $\bar{D}_{Xe-Cl} =$ two-thirds of $37 \approx 25$ kcal./mole. If this figure is combined with Δh_1 (57.9 kcal./mole), then ΔH_f^0 for $XeCl_2(g) \approx 58 - 50 \approx$

8 kcal./mole, i.e., the formation of $XeCl_2$ from its elements in the gas phase is endothermic.

An estimate of the (unfavorable) entropy change ΔS^0 accompanying the reaction $Xe(g) + Cl_2(g) \rightarrow XeCl_2(g)$ can be obtained using the following values for the entropy $S^0(25°C.)$ of Xe and Cl_2:

$$S^0\, Xe(g) = 40.53 \text{ cal./deg. per mole}$$
$$Cl_2(g) = 53.29 \text{ cal./deg. per mole}$$

and estimating S^0 for $XeCl_2(g)$ from the empirical equation (13) (see Chapter 1, Section II A 2)

$$S^0 = 39.0 + 0.34M - (6.2 \times 10^{-4})M^2$$

which with M (the molecular weight of $XeCl_2$) = 202.2 gives $S^0(XeCl_2(g))$ = 82.4 cal./deg. per mole, and ΔS^0 for the formation of $XeCl_2(g)$ from its elements = -11 cal./deg. per mole, and $T . \Delta S$ ($T = 298°K.$) = -3 kcal./mole.

Therefore,

$$\Delta G^0 = \Delta H^0 - T . \Delta S^0$$
$$= 8 - (-3)$$
$$= 11 \text{ kcal./mole}$$

which corresponds to an equilibrium constant K_p for the gas-phase reaction $Xe + Cl_2 \rightarrow XeCl_2$ of about 10^{-8}.

This result means that $XeCl_2$ is unlikely to be formed from its elements under ordinary conditions. The possibility of its formation from other reactants and other conditions is not excluded however, and whether or not it would survive under ordinary conditions would of course depend on the lack of a favorable decomposition mechanism, i.e., on kinetic factors.

III. NOBLE-GAS COMPOUNDS DERIVED FROM THEIR UNIPOSITIVE CATIONS

The compounds $XePtF_6$ (2) and $XeRhF_6$ (14) appear to be salts derived from the unipositive cation Xe^+, and it is profitable to investigate the circumstances in which this ion is likely to be thermodynamically stable in a crystalline lattice. In view of the facts that the dioxygenyl compound $O_2^+PtF_6^-$ is isomorphous with a number of nitrosonium (NO^+) and potassium (K^+) salts like $NOOsF_6$ and $KRuF_6(15)$, and that $XePtF_6$ seems to be clearly related to these salts (Bartlett's (2) estimate of the lattice energy of $XePtF_6$ is similar to that of O_2PtF_6), it is a reasonable approximation to equate the lattice energies of corresponding Xe^+ and K^+ salts. It therefore follows that the heat of formation of a solid Xe^+ salt can be assessed roughly by allowing for the difference between the heats of formation of $Xe^+(g)$ and $K^+(g)$. For example, the heat of formation ΔH_f^0 of a crystalline nitrate $M^+NO_3^-(s)$ is the sum of the following enthalpy terms:

$$M(\text{standard state}) \rightarrow M^+(g)+e \qquad \Delta h_1$$
$$\tfrac{1}{2} N_2(g)+1\tfrac{1}{2} O_2(g)+e \rightarrow NO_3^-(g) \qquad \Delta h_2$$
$$M^+(g)+NO_3^-(g) \rightarrow MNO_3(s) \qquad \Delta h_3$$

For $M = K$ and Xe, Δh_2 is a common term, and Δh_3 is assumed to be the same for both cations. Δh_1 for $M = K$ is

$$
\begin{aligned}
K(s) &\rightarrow K(g) & \Delta h &= 21.5 \text{ kcal./mole} \\
K(g) &\rightarrow K^+(g)+e & \Delta h &= 101.5 \text{ kcal./mole} \\
\hline
K(s) &\rightarrow K^+(g)+e & \Delta h_1 &= 123.0 \text{ kcal./mole}
\end{aligned}
$$

and for $M = Xe$,

$$Xe(g) \rightarrow Xe^+(g)+e \qquad \Delta h_1 = 281.2 \text{ kcal./mole}$$

so that ΔH_f^0 for $XeNO_3$ will be *more endothermic* than ΔH_f^0 for KNO_3 by $281.2 - 123.0 = 158.2$ kcal./mole. Since ΔH_f^0 for $KNO_3(s)$ is -117.8 kcal./mole, it follows that ΔH_f^0 for $XeNO_3$ would be about $-118 + 158 = +40$ cal./mole.

The difference of 158 kcal./mole will hold for all salts of K^+ and Xe^+ in which the anion has a single negative charge; if the anion is doubly charged (e.g., SO_4^{2-}) the difference will be $2 \times 158 = 316$ kcal./mole.

From known heats of formation of potassium salts, the following estimates of heats of formation of Xe^+ salts were obtained:

	M = K$^+$	M = Xe$^+$
MF	-134	$+24$
MCl	-104	$+54$
MBr	-94	$+64$
MI	-78	$+80$
MClO$_4$	-104	$+54$
MNO$_3$	-118	$+40$
MSCN	-49	$+109$
MBF$_4$[a]	-452	-294
MBH$_4$[b]	-55	$+103$
M$_2$SO$_4$	-343	-27
M$_2$CrO$_4$	-338	-22
M$_2$MoO$_4$[c]	-357	-41
M$_2$S$_2$O$_8$	-458	-142
M$_2$SiF$_6$	-671	-355
M$_2$SnCl$_6$	-363	-47

(Data from ref. (16), except [a] ref. (17); [b] ref. (18); [c] ref. (19).)

These estimates are rather crude, but provide an indication of the probable relative stabilities of Xe$^+$ compounds, and suggest that several of them may be formed from their elements quite exothermically, for example, XeBF$_4$, XeSiF$_6$, and Xe$_2$S$_2$O$_8$. As an example of the use of these estimates, the energetic feasibility of preparing xenon tetrafluoroborate, XeBF$_4$, will now be considered. A reasonable preparative process would be

$$Xe(g) + BF_3(g) + \tfrac{1}{2} F_2(g) \rightarrow XeBF_4(s)$$

Since ΔH_f^0 for BF$_3$(g) is -265.4 cal./mole (16), and for XeBF$_4$(s) is -294 kcal./mole (estimated above), then the enthalpy change for the preparative reaction is $-294-(-265) = -29$ kcal./mole, i.e., the reaction is exothermic. To estimate the more significant free energy change (ΔG^0), the entropy of XeBF$_4$ is required, and this can be obtained from Latimer's (16) values:

$$Xe^+ (\text{interpolated}) = 13.5; \quad B^{3+} = 4.9; \quad 4\,F^- = 4 \times 4.7$$

whence S^0, XeBF$_4$(s) = 37.2 cal./deg. per mole, so for the reaction

$$Xe(g) + BF_3(g) + \tfrac{1}{2} F_2(g) \rightarrow XeBF_4(s)$$

S^0 values: 40.5   60.7   24.3   37.2

$$\Delta S^0 = -88.3 \text{ cal./deg. per mole}$$

and

$$\Delta G^0 = \Delta H^0 - T \cdot \Delta S^0$$
$$= -29 - (298 \times -0.0883)$$
$$= -29 + 26 = -3 \text{ kcal./mole}$$

This small negative result suggests that the free energy change for the reaction is close to zero, and that the chances of making the reaction proceed would be enhanced by working at low temperatures (which reduce the unfavorable $T \cdot \Delta S$ term).

The preparation of Xe^+ salts appears to be most likely to succeed with complex fluoro-anions, in which the generally high energy of the bonds formed by fluorine is sufficient to outweigh both the considerable energy necessary to ionize the xenon atoms, and the effect of the unfavorable entropy change associated with the formation of a crystalline solid from gaseous reactants.

The likelihood of formation of salts with unipositive noble-gas cations decreases from xenon to helium; the increased energy required to ionize a smaller noble-gas atom is insufficiently offset by the increase in lattice energy arising from the smaller radius of the noble-gas cation. Calculations similar to the above for krypton (Kr^+) salts using the approximation that their lattice energies are about the same as those of the corresponding sodium salts yield heats of formation for the krypton compounds which are about 20–50 kcal./mole more positive than those of the corresponding xenon compounds.

Of course, there is always the possibility of the existence of noble gas compounds whose free energies of formation are quite highly positive, stability being conferred by kinetic rather than thermodynamic circumstances, i.e., by extremely slow *rates* of decomposition. Noyes (20) has discussed the interesting possibility that neon monoxide NeO is such a compound. On the assumption that the bond energy of NeO is about the same as that of the iso-electronic molecule F_2, Noyes estimated the equilibrium constant K for the reaction

$$2 \text{ Ne(g)} + O_2\text{(g)} \rightarrow 2 \text{ NeO(g)}$$

to be about 10^{-32}. The preparation of NeO from its elements under ordinary conditions is thus out of the question, but from an analysis of the available mechanisms of decomposition, Noyes concluded that NeO, like nitric oxide NO, would be inert to decomposition in spite of its thermodynamic instability, and suggested a possible synthesis from liquid neon and excited (^1D) oxygen atoms.

REFERENCES

(1) Pimentel, G. C., *J. Chem. Phys.*, **19,** 446 (1951).
(2) Bartlett, N., *Proc. Chem. Soc.*, 218 (1962).
(3) Moody, G. J., and J. D. R. Thomas, *J. Roy. Inst. Chem.*, **88,** 31 (1964).
(4) Bartlett, N., *Endevour*, **23,** 3 (1964).
(5) Coulson, C. A., *J. Chem. Soc.*, **1964,** 1442.
(6) Pauling. L., *The Nature of the Chemical Bond*, 3rd ed., Cornell University Press, New York, 1960.
(7) Levy, H. A., and P. A. Agron, *J. Am. Chem. Soc.*, **85,** 241 (1963).
(8) Wiebenga, E. H., E. E. Havinga, and K. A. Boswijk, in H. J. Emeleus and A. G. Sharpe, eds., *Advances in Inorganic Chemistry and Radiochemistry*, Vol. 3, Academic Press, Inc., New York, 1961, p. 133.
(9) Pimentel, G. C., and R. D. Spratley, *J. Am. Chem. Soc.*, **85,** 826 (1963).
(10) Svec, H. J., and G. D. Flesch, *Science*, **142,** 954 (1963).
(11) Mulliken, R. S., *J. Chem. Phys.*, **2,** 782 (1934); **3,** 573 (1935).
(12) Lewis, G. N., and M. Randall, *Thermodynamics*, revised by K. S. Pitzer and L. Brewer, 2nd ed., McGraw-Hill, New York, 1961.
(13) Kubaschewski, O., and E. L. Evans, *Metallurgical Thermochemistry*, Pergamon Press Ltd., London, 1956, p. 195.
(14) Bartlett, N., N. K. Jha, P. R. Rao, and M. Booth, reported in *Chem. Eng. News*, February 4, 1963, p. 38.
(15) Bartlett, N., and D. H. Lohmann, *J. Chem. Soc.*, **1962,** 5253.
(16) Latimer, W. M., *Oxidation Potentials*, 2nd ed., Prentice-Hall, Inc., New York, 1952.
(17) Bills, J. L., and F. A. Cotton, *J. Phys. Chem.*, **64,** 1477 (1960).
(18) Johnson, W. H., R. H. Schumm, I. H. Wilson, and E. J. Prosen, *J. Res. Nat. Bur. Std.*, **65A,** 97 (1961).
(19) Nelson, T., C. Moss, and L. G. Helper, *J. Phys. Chem.*, **64,** 376 (1960).
(20) Noyes, R. M., *J. Am. Chem. Soc.*, **85,** 2202 (1963).

Chapter 8

Miscellaneous

I. PH$_5$, SH$_6$, AND RELATED COMPOUNDS

In the group 5 sequence of elements N, P, As, Sb, and Bi, the formation of 5-covalent compounds MX$_5$ is not observed where M = nitrogen (as discussed in Chapter 2), and such compounds are often unstable where M = arsenic (as discussed in Chapter 6, Section I A), and where M = bismuth (and to some extent antimony), as discussed in Chapter 5, Section IV. Phosphorus however forms a familiar group of PX$_5$ compounds, including the three pentahalides PF$_5$, PCl$_5$, and PBr$_5$, and even phosphorus pentaphenyl, P(C$_6$H$_5$)$_5$. It is therefore surprising that phosphorus (V) hydride, PH$_5$, has never been prepared. The iodide PI$_5$ is the only "missing" pentahalide. The energetic factors influencing the readiness with which a molecule PX$_5$ is formed from the tervalent molecule PX$_3$ are best appreciated by considering its stepwise formation in the following way:

(1) $X_2 \rightarrow 2\,X$ (X = F, Cl, Br, I, H)

(2) $PX_3 + 2\,X \rightarrow PX_5$

Step (1) is the endothermic fission of the X—X covalent bond. Step (2) is the exothermic combination of the PX$_3$ molecule with two X atoms to form PX$_5$, and is actually the resultant of two processes — first the (endothermic) excitation of the valence electrons in PX$_3$ and X to orbitals suitable for bond formation, and second, the (exothermic) combination of the excited species to form PX$_5$ molecules.

The factors which favor the formation of PX$_5$ are thus

153

(a) a low X—X bond energy;

(b) low excitation energies for PX_3 and for X; and

(c) a high "intrinsic" energy for the two new P—X bonds.

In respect to the first of these, factor (a), hydrogen is at a disadvantage compared with all four halogens, because the H—H covalent bond is an exceptionally strong one, as the following data establish

$$X_2(g) \rightarrow 2\,X(g), \qquad \Delta H, (25°C.), \qquad kcal./mole\ of\ X_2$$

X =	H	F	Cl	Br	I
	104.2	37.8	57.9	53.5	51.0

The influence of factors (b) and (c) is more difficult to establish quantitatively. The average bond energies (Table 1.9) in the tervalent molecules PH_3 (76.4 kcal./mole) and PCl_3 (79.1 kcal./mole) do not differ much, and suggest that the P—H and P—Cl bonds may be of comparable strengths in the PX_5 molecules. If this is the case, the failure to prepare PH_5 is largely a consequence of factor (a), i.e., the high H—H bond energy. However, there is some dispute as to the electronic structure of PX_5, and hence as to the magnitude of the excitation energies which determine factor (b). The problem centers on the degree of involvement of the phosphorus $3d$ orbitals in the P—X bonds in PX_5. We have seen (Chapter 2, Section I) that the $3s^2 3p^3 \rightarrow 3s^1 3p^3 3d^1$ transition in the isolated phosphorus atom is endothermic by about 14 e.v.; this promotion energy, although smaller than that for the $2s^2 2p^3 \rightarrow 2s^1 2p^3 3d^1$ transition in nitrogen, is sufficiently large to require that the bonds formed by the resulting $sp^3 d$ hybrid orbitals be very strong, if PX_5 formation is to be energetically feasible. Overlap integral calculations, using Slater-type functions to describe the phosphorus atom orbitals, have shown (1) that in the *isolated* P atom the $3d$ orbitals are too diffuse to bond effectively. Also Pauling (2) has expressed the view that in PF_5, only four covalent bonds are formed using the $3s$ and $3p$ orbitals; the fifth phosphorus electron is removed and distributed over the five electronegative fluorine atoms, so that the structure can be described as a resonance hybrid of forms such as

If the concept of $3d$ orbital participation is to be retained, it must be shown that the $3d$ orbitals of the isolated phosphorus atom are modified in some way to give more effective overlap and better bonding. Craig and Magnusson (1) have shown that highly electronegative ligands such as F attract charge away from the phosphorus atom, causing contraction of the $3d$ orbitals to a state of compactness suitable for bond formation. This $3d$ orbital contraction is associated with an actual *increase* in promotion energy, and the extent to which this is counterbalanced by stronger bond formation is quantitatively uncertain.

Whatever view of the bonding is accepted, it seems that a requirement for PX_5 formation is that X be at least moderately electronegative. The electronegativities of the halogens and hydrogen, according to Pauling (3), are as follows:

F	Cl	Br	I	H
4.0	3.0	2.8	2.5	2.1

It is significant that PX_5 molecules are formed only where X = F, Cl, and Br. Failure to prepare PH_5 would therefore seem to be due to the high H—H bond energy, coupled with the fact that the hydrogen atom is insufficiently electronegative *either* to stabilize ionic structures like

$$
\begin{array}{ccc}
\text{H} & & \text{H}^- \\
& \diagdown & \\
\text{H} & \!\!\!-\text{P}^+ & \\
& \diagup \ \diagdown & \\
\text{H} & & \text{H}
\end{array}
$$

(if $3d$ orbital participation is not admitted), *or* to perturb the $3d$ orbitals sufficiently to cause their contraction and effective participation in hybrids suitable for bond formation.

The role of $3d$ orbitals in PX_5 molecules has been reviewed by Hudson (4).

Similar problems are encountered in explaining the nonexistence of hexa-covalent derivatives of sulfur other than the hexafluoride, e.g., SH_6 and SCl_6 have not been prepared. The high H—H bond energy will certainly contribute to the instability of SH_6, but in the case of SCl_6 recourse must again be had to arguments based on an inadequate electronegativity of chlorine.

II. DIMERIC FORMS OF BORON TRIHALIDES AND TRIALKYLS

It is well-known that aluminum chloride, bromide, and iodide readily form dimeric molecules Al_2X_6 (X = Cl, Br, I) under a variety of conditions; aluminum trimethyl is also dimeric. The molecular dimensions of $Al_2Cl_6(5)$ and $Al_2(CH_3)_6$ (6) molecules are as follows:

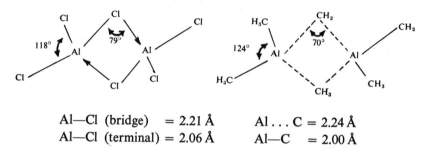

$$Al—Cl \text{ (bridge)} = 2.21 \text{ Å} \qquad Al \ldots C = 2.24 \text{ Å}$$
$$Al—Cl \text{ (terminal)} = 2.06 \text{ Å} \qquad Al—C = 2.00 \text{ Å}$$

The corresponding boron compounds — BCl_3, BBr_3, BI_3, and $B(CH_3)_3$ — occur only as monomers under ordinary conditions, i.e., their vapor densities are normal and no significant association has been reported to occur in solution. The reasons for this are sought in the following discussion of the energetics of the dimerization process.

Since the reaction

$$2 BX_3(g) \rightarrow B_2X_6(g)$$

would be accompanied by a decrease in entropy, it is obvious that, for the process to proceed significantly to the right, the dimerization must occur exothermically, as it in fact does in the case of aluminum:

$$2 AlX_3(g) \rightarrow Al_2X_6(g)$$

$\Delta H(25°C.)$, kcal./mole of Al_2X_6

X = Cl	−29.0	ref. (7)
Br	−26.6	ref. (7)
I	−22.3	ref. (7)
CH_3	−20.2	ref. (8)

The bond strengths in monomer and dimer must therefore be of prime importance in accounting for the failure of BX_3 molecules to dimerize. It is probable that the B—X bonds in the boron trihalides are not simply single bonds of the sigma type. Since the BX_3 molecules are without exception planar in configuration, it is possible to regard the boron atom as using three trigonal sp^2 hybrid orbitals for sigma bond formation, leaving the vacant $2p_z$ orbital (at right angles to the trigonal plane) free to accept the equivalent of a total of two electrons donated by the p_π orbitals of the bonded halogen atoms. In valence-bond terminology, this amounts to contributions from double-bonded canonical structures like

$$
\begin{array}{c}
X^+ \\
\parallel \\
B^- \\
\diagup\quad\diagdown \\
X\qquad\quad X
\end{array}
$$

so that each B—X bond consists of a sigma component and a fractional-order π-component. Since the extent of halogen back-coordination would be expected to decrease with increasing size of halogen, the proportion of double-bond character in the B—X bond should decrease along the series X = F, Cl, Br, I. Bond-length data (9) are in accord with such a trend.

In the formation of a dimer, this π-bond stabilization of the B—X bonds is lost because the fourth orbital on boron must be used to accept the electron pair from the bridge-forming halogen atom of the second molecule. This effect is readily recognizable in the conversion of BF_3 to $BF_3 \cdot NH_3$. In the latter compound the fourth orbital of boron is used to accept the nitrogen atom lone pair, and the B—F distance is 1.38 Å (9), which is significantly longer than that (1.295 Å) in BF_3 itself because the bond-shortening effect of π-bonding has been removed. Lipscomb (10) has suggested that this back-coordination stabilizes the trihalide monomer BX_3 relative to the dimer B_2X_6 sufficiently to prevent the formation of the latter.

It is not so readily seen why, on this basis, boron trimethyl $B(CH_3)_3$ should not dimerize. Perhaps, as Coulson (11) suggests, the electron-donating property of the methyl group provides (by "hyperconjugation") sufficient π-electrons to fill the vacant boron orbital.

There is some doubt, however, as to whether the stabilization of the BX_3 monomers by π-bonding is an adequate explanation of their failure to dimerize, and it is profitable to analyze the energy terms contributing to the enthalpy change ΔH for the process

$$2\,BX_3(g) \rightarrow B_2X_6(g)$$

These can be visualized as follows:

(1) the absorption of energy as the fourth boron orbital in the monomer is disengaged from π-bonding;

(2) the energy change accompanying the rearrangement of the single p_z and three sp^2 orbitals in the trigonal monomer to give four approximately tetrahedral sp^3 hybrid orbitals in the dimer; and

(3) the liberation of energy as two new bridging B—X bonds are formed in the dimer.

Dimerization would be expected if the heat liberated in (3) is sufficient to outweigh the net heat absorption of steps (1) and (2), which together can be regarded as constituting a "reorganization energy" term. Cotton and Leto (12) have estimated this reorganization energy for most of the boron and aluminum halides, and their results are as follows:

Reorganization energies, kcal./mole.

(= sums of π-bond energies and the energy change in the σ-bonds on adjustment from sp^2 to sp^3 hybridization.)

BF_3	BCl_3	BBr_3
48.3	30.3	26.2

	$AlCl_3$	$AlBr_3$	AlI_3
	31.6	27.9	18.7

These values, which are only approximations, do however suggest that there may be no great difference between boron and aluminum in respect to reorganization energy, and if this is the case then the failure of BX_3 molecules to dimerize is presumably related to an inadequate strength in the bridging B—X—B bonds.

It is interesting that when two boron trihalides such as BF_3 and BCl_3 are mixed, rapid equilibration occurs to give a mixture of the pure trihalides together with the mixed species BF_2Cl and $BFCl_2$, which have been identified by their Raman spectra (13) and by NMR studies (14). The mixed halides generally disproportionate to the pure trihalides if their isolation is attempted. It is possible that the halogen redistribution process occurs through the formation of halogen-bridged dimers (13, 15), for example but positive identification of such a dimer has not yet been reported.

III. COMPOUNDS OF MOLECULAR NITROGEN ANALOGOUS TO THE CARBONYLS

The diatomic molecule N_2 is very unreactive chemically. Its physical properties (melting point, boiling point, density, critical temperature and pressure, et cetera) resemble very closely those of the iso-electronic molecule carbon monoxide, CO, but the two substances differ sharply in reactivity. In particular, carbon monoxide forms many derivatives, the metallic carbonyls, in which a bond is formed between the CO molecule and a transition-metal atom like Cr, Fe, Co, or Ni. Familiar examples are $Ni(CO)_4$ and $Fe(CO)_5$.

Superficially the nitrogen molecule is electronically equipped to form similar compounds, and it is therefore surprising that none has ever been isolated. The reasons for this seem to be as follows.

Both N_2 and CO contain a total of ten electrons in the valence shells of the bonded atoms, and their structural similarity is evident from the triple-bonded formulas

$$:N \equiv N: \quad \text{and} \quad :\overset{-}{C} \equiv \overset{+}{O}:$$

Extensive molecular-orbital treatments of both molecules have appeared (16, 17) and a simplified qualitative description has been given by Jaffé and Orchin (18).

The electron configurations of the atoms concerned are $C = 1s^2 2s^2 2p^2$; $N = 1s^2 2s^2 2p^3$; and $O = 1s^2 2s^2 2p^4$. In principle the three bonds in N_2 and CO can be constructed using only the three $2p$ orbitals of each atom, so that the nonbonding pair on each atom occupies a spherically symmetrical $2s$ orbital. It is found however that the sigma component of the triple bond is strengthened if a mixture of $2s$ and $2p$ orbitals is used for its formation. In the case of the N_2 molecule, only a small proportion of s-character is required for this purpose, so that the

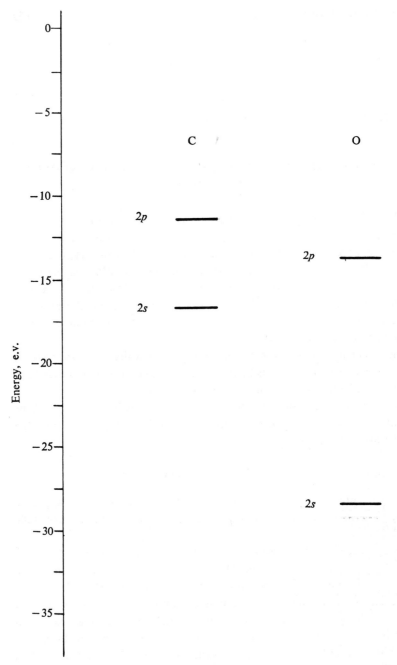

Figure 8.1. Energy levels of atomic orbitals of carbon and oxygen.

unshared pairs occupy orbitals which are still essentially — approximately 70–80% (18, 19) — s in character. The situation is different in CO however, because the bonded atoms are no longer identical and the energies of the $2s$ and $2p$ orbitals no longer correspond exactly. The approximate energies of the $2s$ and $2p$ orbitals of carbon and oxygen (20) are shown in Figure 8.1. In order that the sp hybrid orbitals used to form the sigma bond should combine effectively, it is necessary that their energies be similar, and this can only be achieved if the sp hybrid orbital of the carbon atom has mainly $2s$ character, and the sp hybrid orbital of the oxygen atom has mainly $2p$ character. This means that the *nonbonding* (lone pair) sp hybrid orbital remaining on carbon has mainly — about 68 % (18) — $2p$ character, while the nonbonding (lone pair) sp hybrid orbital remaining on oxygen has mainly — about 78 % (18) — $2s$ character. It therefore appears that the lone electron pairs on the nitrogen atoms in N_2, like that on the oxygen atom in CO, are located in essentially nondirectional orbitals, while the lone pair on the carbon atom in CO is directed in space and is more capable of forming a covalent bond with a suitable acceptor atom. (The directional character of the lone pair on carbon, insofar as it compensates for the higher electronegativity of the oxygen atom, may be an important factor in determining the very small dipole moment of the CO molecule.)

There is evidence however that the carbon-to-metal bond in say $Ni(CO)_4$ is not simply a sigma-bond formed by donation of the lone pair C-atom electrons into a vacant Ni-atom orbital (21), for CO is a very weak Lewis base, and fails to form complexes with common acceptor species (Lewis acids) like boron or aluminum halides. It is therefore likely that the charge which would accumulate on the metal atom as a result of CO electron donation is transferred back to the ligand by overlap of a filled $3d$ orbital of the metal with a vacant π^* antibonding orbital of the CO molecule. There is thus a two-way process of charge transfer. Orgel (21) has pointed out that if a lone pair electron is transferred from the carbon atom of the CO molecule to the metal atom, and simultaneously an electron is transferred from the metal to a π^* antibonding orbital of CO, an excited CO molecule is obtained in the same electronic state as that resulting from an internal excitation of an electron from the carbon atom lone pair orbital to a π^* antibonding orbital. The energy of such a transition is thus a guide to the likelihood of the occurrence of complex-formation with metals, and is about 6 e.v. for CO. The corresponding energy for N_2 is 7.3 e.v., and this factor must be considered, along with the nondirectional nature of the lone pair orbitals, as relevant to the failure of the N_2 molecule to form carbonyl-like coordination compounds.

It is interesting to consider the possibility of the N_2 molecule using its π electrons for dative bond formation and adopting a "side-on" position with respect to a metal:

$$M \leftarrow \begin{matrix} N \\ ||| \\ N \end{matrix}$$

This type of bonding is known in complexes formed by the analogously triple-bonded acetylenes $R—C\equiv C—R$ and cyanides $R—C\equiv N$, and is conceivable (though unknown) in carbonyls. Orgel (21) considers it likely that the structure

$$M \leftarrow \begin{matrix} N \\ ||| \\ N \end{matrix}$$

is favored relative to

$$M \leftarrow N\equiv N$$

to a greater degree than

$$M \leftarrow \begin{matrix} C \\ ||| \\ O \end{matrix}$$

is favored relative to

$$M \leftarrow C\equiv O$$

although it is not known which of the two $M—N_2$ structures would be the more stable on an absolute scale.

It is conceivable that metal ion $—N_2$ complexes are intermediates in the biological process of nitrogen fixation.

IV. IODIDES OF SULFUR AND SELENIUM

A. Sulfur Iodides

In 1950 Sidgwick (22) reported that sulfur iodides did not exist, and that there was no evidence that various solid phases reported to contain such compounds were anything more than solid solutions of iodine in sulfur. It is still true that no sulfur iodide has been isolated in a pure state, but there is evidence that unstable sulfur iodides can be prepared in solution. For example, Rao (23) and Murthy (24) showed that solutions of S_2Cl_2 or SCl_2 in carbon tetrachloride, on treatment with powdered potassium iodide or anhydrous hydrogen iodide, underwent a series of color changes, attributed to sulfur iodide formation, before the violet color of the decomposition product (iodine) appeared. Féher and Münzer claim (25) to have identified S_2I_2, S_3I_2, S_4I_2, S_5I_2, and S_6I_2 spectrophotometrically in dilute solutions obtained by treating the corresponding sulfur chlorides S_nCl_2 dissolved in cyclohexane with powdered potassium iodide. The same authors have also given a summary of the early literature.

B. Selenium Iodides

The situation with respect to iodides of selenium is very similar to that described above for sulfur. No pure compound has been isolated, but the formation of selenium iodides in solution is suggested by the facts that elemental selenium dissolves in carbon tetrachloride only in the presence of iodine, and that the absorption spectra of carbon disulfide solutions of selenium and iodine are not additive on mixing (26). Spectrophotometric evidence for the formation of an unstable selenium iodide when a solution of Se_2Cl_2 in carbon tetrachloride is shaken with potassium iodide at $-14°C$. was also obtained by Rao (27).

The iodides of sulfur and selenium have been included by Pauling (28) in the group of compounds whose constituent elements are very similar in electronegativity and consequently rather unstable with respect to their elements: other examples are NCl_3, CI_4, and PH_3. Pauling's postulate (see Chapter 1, Section II C is that when a bond is formed between two atoms A and B which differ in electronegativity, the bond is stabilized by ionic-covalent resonance to an extent Δ, given by

$$\Delta = \bar{D}_{A-B} - \tfrac{1}{2}(\bar{D}_{A-A} + \bar{D}_{B-B})$$

If the two atoms A and B have identical (or very similar) electronegativities, there is no (or little) ionic-covalent resonance stabilization of the bond A—B and hence little tendency for it to be formed in preference to the bonds A—A and B—B in the elements, in other words, the heat of formation of the compound between A and B from the elements is likely to be close to zero.

Pauling's electronegativity coefficients (Table 1.10) for the elements concerned are

	S	Se	I
	2.5	2.4	2.5

and on this basis it can be understood why the iodides of sulfur and selenium (and of carbon, whose Pauling coefficient = 2.5) have a low stability with respect to decomposition into their elements.

V. ANALOGUES OF THE MERCUROUS ION, Hg_2^{2+}

Compounds containing the mercurous ion Hg^+—Hg^+ are well-known, and many are stable in the solid state and some in aqueous solution. Evidence for a similar ion in compounds of zinc and cadmium is exiguous; indeed recent authorities (29) have described the mercurous ion as unique.

What appears to be an authentic compound containing the analogous Cd_2^{2+} ion has been prepared by Corbett and his co-workers (30, 31). When a mixture of $CdCl_2 + 2\,AlCl_3$ is fused, a phase $Cd^{2+}(AlCl_4^-)_2$ is formed which was identified as a distinct species rather than a mixture by its X-ray diffraction powder diagram. Addition of Cd metal to this substance leads to the separation of a phase of empirical composition $CdAlCl_4$, which was formulated $(Cd^+$—$Cd^+)$ $(AlCl_4^-)_2$ on the basis of its diamagnetism; also its Raman spectrum contained lines corresponding to the anion $AlCl_4^-$, and a frequency $\nu = 183$ cm.$^{-1}$ which was assigned to the Cd_2^{2+} ion stretching vibration on the basis of its relatively high intensity, although ν_4 of the $AlCl_4^-$ ion in fused $NaAlCl_4$ is at 180 cm.$^{-1}$, but of low intensity (32).

The bond-stretching force constant for Cd^+—Cd^+ was estimated to be 1.11 millidynes/Å, compared with 2.52 millidynes/Å estimated for Hg^+—Hg^+ in a similar environment: the cadmium-to-cadmium bond is thus weak by comparison with the corresponding mercury bond.

It is interesting to consider the factors likely to stabilize the ion Cd^+—Cd^+, or even Zn^+—Zn^+, that is, the factors likely to displace the equilibrium

$$M^{2+} + M \rightleftharpoons M_2^{2+}$$

to the right-hand side. In the case of mercury (M = Hg), the conversion of Hg^{2+} to Hg_2^{2+} can be carried out in aqueous solution, showing that the mercuric ion Hg^{2+} is not sufficiently stabilized by the coordinated water molecules to prevent its reduction. If other complexing species such as cyanide ion CN^- or iodide ion I^- are present however, the Hg^{II} cyano- and iodo- complexes are sufficiently stable to resist reduction, also, solutions of the mercurous ion Hg_2^{2+} disproportionate when treated with I^- or CN^-:

$$Hg_2^{2+} + 4\,I^- \rightarrow HgI_4^{2-} + Hg$$

There are very few ligands which do not cause this disproportionation; they include pyrophosphate, oxalate, and succinate ions (33). The ease with which the reduction

$$Hg^{2+} + Hg \rightarrow Hg_2^{2+}$$

can be accomplished is therefore dependent on the solvent used and the nature of the anion present — both must be chosen so that excessive stabilization of Hg^{2+} is avoided.

In the case of $M = Cd$, no reduction of Cd^{2+} to Cd_2^{2+} has been achieved in aqueous solutions; the compound $Cd_2(AlCl_4)_2$ disproportionates and precipitates metallic cadmium on contact with water. Corbett (30, 31) therefore used melts in place of aqueous solutions for the preparation of $Cd_2(AlCl_4)_2$, and the anion $AlCl_4^-$ was chosen to avoid the strong Cd^{2+}-anion interaction evident if Cl^- alone is present.

Additional factors influencing the conversion

$$CdX_2 + Cd \rightarrow Cd_2X_2$$

are the lattice energies of the solids CdX_2 and Cd_2X_2. Presumably CdX_2 will have the higher lattice energy since in Cd_2X_2 the ion Cd_2^{2+} has the same charge as, but is much bigger than, the ion Cd^{2+}. The problem is then to minimize this lattice energy difference, and how this may be achieved is not easy to discern. If $X = $ a halide, then increasing the size halide may decrease the lattice energy difference in accordance with van Arkel's view (34) that the effect of increased halide size in a series of halides of a given element is to decrease the difference in lattice energies between the two different states, provided no change in structure occurs. However, the effect of increasing halide size in the case of mercurous halides appears to be to lengthen (and hence weaken) the Hg—Hg bond in the mercurous ion, as the following bond-length data (35, 36) show:

Hg—Hg distance in Hg_2^{2+} ion, Å	
Hg_2F_2	2.43
Hg_2Cl_2	2.53
Hg_2Br_2	2.58
Hg_2I_2	2.69

Also, it has been suggested (33) that covalent-bond formation between a ligand such as I^- and a mercury atom of the Hg_2^{2+} ion diminishes the amount of s-character in the Hg—Hg bond and thus weakens it, and the most stable mercurous compounds are those in which the anionic component is least likely to form covalent bonds (e.g., F^-, $P_2O_7^{4-}$). If this is also true of the Cd_2^{2+} ion, then the chances of preparing compounds containing this ion (or even Zn_2^{2+}) would be enhanced by the choice of stable anions like F^- or $P_2O_7^{4-}$ as the crystal partners for Cd_2^{2+}. This view is supported by the fact that $AlCl_4^-$ is the anion present in Corbett's Cd_2^{2+} compound.

The broad aspects of metal-to-metal bonding, which is not uncommon among complex compounds of the transition metals, have been discussed by Coffey, Lewis, and Nyholm (37).

REFERENCES

(1) Craig, D. P., and E. A. Magnusson, *J. Chem. Soc.*, **1956**, 4895.
(2) Pauling, L., *The Nature of the Chemical Bond*, 3rd ed., Cornell University Press, New York, 1960, p. 145.
(3) ref. (2), p. 90.
(4) Hudson, R. F., in H. J. Emeleus and A. G. Sharpe, eds., *Advances in Inorganic Chemistry and Radiochemistry*, Vol. 5, Academic Press, Inc., New York, 1963, p. 351.
(5) Palmer, K. J., and N. Elliott, *J. Am. Chem. Soc.*, **60**, 1852 (1938).
(6) Lewis, P. H., and R. E. Rundle, *J. Chem. Phys.*, **21**, 986 (1953).
(7) Fischer, W., and O. Rahlfs, *Z. Anorg. Allgem. Chem.*, **205**, 1 (1932).
(8) Laubengayer, A. W., and W. E. Gilliam. *J. Am. Chem. Soc.*, **63**, 477 (1941).
(9) ref. (2), p. 318.
(10) Lipscomb, W. N., in H. J. Emeleus and A. G. Sharpe, eds., *Advances in Inorganic Chemistry and Radiochemistry*, Vol. 1, Academic Press, Inc., New York, 1959, p. 147.
(11) Coulson, C. A., *Valence*, Oxford University Press, London, 1953, p. 318.
(12) Cotton, F. A., and J. R. Leto, *J. Chem. Phys.*, **30**, 993 (1959).
(13) Long, D. H., and D. Dollimore, *J. Chem. Soc.*, **1954**, 4457.

(14) Coyle, T. D., and F. G. A. Stone, *J. Chem. Phys.*, **32,** 1892 (1960).
(15) Cotton, F. A., and G. Wilkinson, *Advanced Inorganic Chemistry*, Interscience, New York, 1962, p. 189.
(16) Scherr, C. W., *J. Chem. Phys.*, **23,** 569 (1955).
(17) Sahni, R. S., *Trans. Faraday Soc.*, **49,** 1246 (1953).
(18) Jaffé, H. H., and M. Orchin, *Tetrahedron*, **10,** 212 (1960).
(19) Pauling, L., *Tetrahedron*, **17,** 229 (1962).
(20) Jaffé, H. H., *J. Chem. Educ.*, **33,** 25 (1956).
(21) Orgel, L. E., *An Introduction to Transition-metal Chemistry*, Methuen and Co., Ltd., London, 1960.
(22) Sidgwick, N. V., *The Chemical Elements and their Compounds*, Vol. 2, Oxford University Press, London, 1950.
(23) Rao, M. R. A., *Proc. Indian Acad. Sci.*, **11A,** 162, 175 (1940); *Chem. Abstr.* **34,** 7179 (1940).
(24) Murthy, A. R. V., *Proc. Indian Acad. Sci.*, **37A,** 17 (1953); *Chem. Abstr.*, **47,** 12084 (1953).
(25) Féher, F., and H. Münzer, *Ber.*, **96,** 1150 (1963).
(26) McCullough, J. D., *J. Am. Chem. Soc.*, **61,** 3401 (1939).
(27) Rao, M. R. A., *Proc. Indian Acad. Sci.*, **12A,** 410 (1940); *Chem. Abstr.*, **35,** 2805 (1941).
(28) Pauling, L., *General Chemistry*, W. H. Freeman and Co., San Francisco, 1947, p. 544.
(29) ref. (15), p. 470.
(30) Corbett, J. D., W. J. Durkhard, and L. F. Druding, *J. Am. Chem. Soc.*, **83,** 76 (1961).
(31) Corbett, J. D., *Inorg. Chem.*, **1,** 700 (1962).
(32) Gerding, H., and H. Houtgraaf, *Rec. Trav. Chim.*, **72,** 21 (1953).
(33) Yamane, T., and N. Davidson, *J. Am. Chem. Soc.*, **81,** 4438 (1959).
(34) Van Arkel, A., *Research*, **2,** 307 (1949).
(35) Grdenic, D., *J. Chem. Soc.*, **1956,** 1312.
(36) Grdenic, D., and C. Djordjevic, *J. Chem. Soc.*, **1956,** 1316.
(37) Coffey, C. E., J. Lewis, and R. S. Nyholm, *J. Chem. Soc.*, **1964,** 1741.

AUTHOR INDEX

Numbers in parentheses are reference numbers and indicate that an author's work is referred to although his name is not cited in the text. Numbers in italics give the page on which the complete reference is listed.

SUBJECT INDEX